REPRODUCTION IN
THE INSECTS

REPRODUCTION IN THE INSECTS

by

K. G. DAVEY

Director, Institute of Parasitology
Macdonald College, McGill University, Canada

W. H. FREEMAN AND COMPANY
SAN FRANCISCO

First published ... 1965

© 1965, K. G. Davey

Printed and published in Great Britain
by Oliver and Boyd Ltd., Edinburgh

Preface

This little book is one of a series which, it is hoped, will acquaint the undergraduate and the graduate with various aspects of animal biology. As such it assumes an elementary knowledge of various aspects of general biology and, in the case of the present volume, some acquaintance with the anatomy and classification of insects. Insects are a diverse group, and in no other system is this diversity more strikingly revealed than in the reproductive system. Obviously a book as short as this one can only note that such diversity exists; there has been no attempt to document it.

On the other hand, the functional aspects of the subject—the physiology of reproduction in insects—are more susceptible to treatment in a short book, and it is from this point of view that the subject has been approached. Even here the treatment must be selective rather than exhaustive and the author is only too conscious that there are areas which some may feel should merit closer examination.

The figures have been redrawn by my wife, Jenny. Some of the drawings are original, but most have been taken from the literature; acknowledgements are made to the authors concerned where the figures appear in the text. I am indebted to the McGraw-Hill Book Company for permission to copy drawings appearing in figures 4 and 17 from *Principles of Insect Morphology* by R. E. Snodgrass and to the Ronald Press for permission to copy the drawing in figure 21 from *The Embryology of the Viviparous Insects* by H. R. Hagan. In many cases it has been necessary to simplify the figures somewhat in order to suit the requirements of this elementary text, but every effort has been made to retain the essential accuracy of the originals.

I am grateful to various individuals for their cooperation and assistance. Dr H. E. Hinton of Bristol University has helped in many ways; in particular he was kind enough to let me see unpublished manuscripts on reproduction in insects. This book was conceived, and partially written, while I was working in the Zoology Laboratory of Cambridge University. To my colleagues there I owe a great deal; most especially am I conscious of my indebtedness to Professor Wigglesworth. The arduous tasks of typing, checking references, reading proofs and so on have been admirably executed by Miss J. L. Smith, Miss Joyce Hartnell and Mrs Shirley Baynes of this Institute. All of these people have contributed much to any merit which this volume may have, but the author, of course, accepts full responsibility for any errors.

K. G. D.

Institute of Parasitology
McGill University
January, 1964

Contents

Glossary of Some Anatomical Terms Used in This Book

THE MALE SYSTEM

AEDEAGUS: Typically a sclerotized tube forming most of the intromittent organ. Usually surrounds the endophallus.

BULBUS EJACULATORIUS: A paired, or sometimes single median, glandular organ at the junction of the ejaculatory duct and the vas deferens. It embodies the ectadenes or ectodermal accessory glands of the male.

ECTADENES: The ectodermal accessory glands of the male.

ENDOPHALLUS: The inner part of the intromittent organ, usually invaginated into the end of the aedeagus. Often, but not always, an eversible structure.

GONOPORE: The distal opening of the ejaculatory duct, forming the connection between the internal reproductive ducts and the intromittent organ.

    If the endophallus is eversible out through the phallotreme, the gonopore becomes the functional terminal opening of the intromittent organ.

MESADENES: The mesodermal accessory glands of the male.

MESOMERES: The medial lobes of the divided phallomeres. The two mesomeres usually fuse to form the intromittent organ.

PARAMERES: The lateral lobes of the divided phallomeres. Most often the parameres form clasping organs.

PHALLOMERES: The paired primary ectodermal outgrowths on the ventral surface of the ninth segment. Each of the two phallomeres divides to form a mesomere and a paramere.

PHALLOTREME: The distal opening of the endophallus. It may or may not form the terminal opening of the intromittent organ.

THE FEMALE SYSTEM

BURSA COPULATRIX: The sac-like terminal portion of the female ducts which receives the male genitalia during copulation and which holds the spermatophore.

DUCTUS SEMINALIS: In those Lepidoptera in which oviduct and bursa copulatrix open to the outside separately, the ductus seminalis connects the bursa to the spermatheca.

RECEPTACULUM SEMINIS: The term applied by some Lepidopterists to the organ which functions as the spermatheca.

SPERMALEGE: A special organ (the organ of Berlese of many authors) in various positions on the abdomens of some female Cimicoidea which is pierced by the male and which receives the semen.

SPERMATHECA: Typically a diverticulum of the bursa or common oviduct which functions as a reservoir for the semen. Not all of the organs which function in this way are homologous. It is often accompanied by its own glandular tissue.

VALVIFERS: Two pairs of sclerotized plates, the first valvifers on segment 8, the second valvifers on segment 9, which, together with the valvulae, make up the ovipositor.

VALVULAE: Three pairs of processes, which, together with the valvifers to which they are attached, form the ovipositor. The first valvulae are associated with the first valvifers, while the second and third valvulae are associated with the second valvifers.

1 : Problems

Insects are land animals; from the point of view of numbers and variety, they are the most successful group of terrestrial animals. The exact origin of the insect line is a matter for speculation, but in the course of their emergence from water on to land the evolving insects encountered a number of problems. Their success in solving these problems is a measure of their success as land animals. The various insects have evolved roughly the same sort of mechanisms to overcome the problems associated with a dry environment—an impermeable cuticle, more efficient sense organs and a nitrogen metabolism which permits the elaboration of nearly dry nitrogenous wastes.

Most aquatic animals simply shed their gametes into the water where the eggs are fertilized and where development takes place. The gametes of terrestrial animals remain aquatic organisms and as such they must be provided with the appropriate environment in which to function. For a fully terrestrial animal, internal fertilization is a *sine qua non* for reproduction.

A developing embryo is also essentially an aquatic organism and it too must be provided with a suitable environment. The eggs of most insects develop outside the mother, a mode of reproduction which has achieved success largely because of the evolution of an impermeable chorion, complete with efficient mechanisms for gaseous exchange. But this chorion, formed as it is within the ovaries before fertilization occurs, creates fresh problems associated with the entry of the spermatozoa into the egg.

1

Another factor in the success of the invasion of land by insects has been their impressive potential for an explosive increase in the population of a particular species when the conditions are favourable. Most, but not all, insects reproduce in the adult, motile phase. The less motile, larval stages are, in their most extreme forms, simply machines for feeding, preparing for the short, intense period of egg production in the adult. Many insects produce very large numbers of eggs but numbers alone will not account for their ability to exploit an environment rapidly. It is as much a case of timing and distribution, of producing the fertilized eggs at the appropriate time and seeking out an appropriate place in which to deposit them.

This short book, then, should be regarded as an essay on the ways in which insects have solved some of these problems. As such it concentrates on the functional aspects of reproduction. It does not pretend to be an exhaustive review of the subject—the voluminous literature coupled with the variability which is a feature of reproduction in insects make this impossible in so few pages. We have only begun to understand the physiology of the reproductive system, but if this essay succeeds in demonstrating the paucity of our understanding and in drawing attention to areas where research might be fruitful, its purpose will have been served.

2 : The Male System and the Spermatozoa

It is the task of the reproductive system of the male insect to produce and deliver to the female sufficient spermatozoa to fertilize the eggs. The form of the male reproductive system is, of course, variable from species to species, but that of the blood-sucking bug *Rhodnius* (fig. 1) represents the basic plan. The spermatozoa are produced in the paired testes, which in some species are fused into a single median organ. The spermatozoa leave the testis via the vas deferens, and are stored in the seminal vesicles, usually a simple dilation in each of the paired vasa deferentia.

Associated with the vas deferens in most species are various mesodermal accessory glands (mesadenes) with their ducts. In *Rhodnius*, the duct of the accessory glands unites with the vas deferens of each side in the bulbus ejaculatorius which embodies the ectodermal accessory glands (ectadenes). Ultimately, the various ducts lead into the ejaculatory duct and aedeagus or intromittent organ, both of which are lined with cuticle. There are, of course, many variations on this basic plan. In the cockroaches, for instance, the seminal vesicles and various mesodermal accessory glands are clustered in a single median organ, the mushroom body (fig. 2). In most insects, the spermatozoa are produced in the pupal or penultimate instar and in the adults of many species, including cockroaches, the testis is not a very prominent organ.

Each testis is usually covered by a connective tissue capsule enclosing the testicular tubules or follicles, which vary in number from species to species. The wall of the testicular tubule is a simple epithelial sheath, and the tubule itself can be divided into a number of zones.[129] Thus, the most distal part of the tubule is the germarium which produces the spermatogonia. One to several

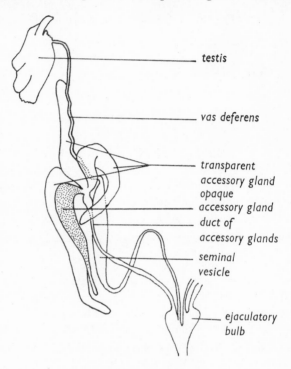

testis

vas deferens

transparent
accessory gland
opaque
accessory gland
duct of
accessory glands
seminal
vesicle

ejaculatory
bulb

FIG. 1. Diagram of one side of the male organs of
Rhodnius (after Davey).

spermatogonia are set free from the germarium and become enclosed in a capsule of somatic cells to form the cysts. The spermatocytes may undergo further mitotic divisions in the 'zone of spermatocytes', but eventually the cysts enter the 'zone of maturation and reduction' where the spermatids are produced and finally, the metamorphosis from spermatids to spermatozoa occurs at the most proximal end of the testis, the 'zone of transformation'. While these developmental zones can be recognized in the testes of some insects, it is frequently impossible to distinguish anything but a distal germarium which gives rise to a number of cysts in various stages of development.[27] In general, all of the cells of any one cyst are at the same developmental stage.

In the germarium of most insects can be found a single large apical cell[18, 27] or more rarely, a multinuclear apical complex.[12]

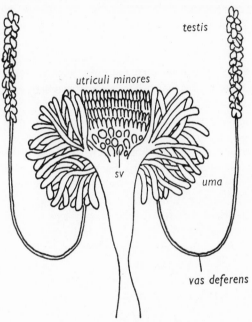

FIG. 2. Ventral view of the male organs of *Periplaneta americana*.

sv, seminal vesicles; *uma*, utriculi majores.

The developing spermatogonia can be seen to cluster around the apical cell, and for this reason it is considered to have a trophic function. Probably the cells of the cyst wall take over this function lower down in the tubule and in Heteroptera certain specialized cells, the trophocytes, situated among the cysts, are thought to nourish the developing germ cells. The cytology of the metamorphosis of spermatids into spermatocytes has been carefully studied in a number of species. The process involves the elongation of the nucleus into a long, slender rod, during which the filamentous nuclear elements become aligned parallel to the long axis of the spermatid.[60, 136] The centriole gives rise to the long filamentous flagellum which has the 9-2 fibrillar structure typical of other flagella.[103] The Golgi body of the spermatid gives rise to a cup-shaped acroblast which secretes a proacrosomal granule which in turn becomes attached to the nucleus at its anterior end. The proacrosomal granule ultimately gives rise to the acrosome itself while the remaining Golgi apparatus is sloughed off with other cytoplasmic elements. In the mature spermatozoon of the house cricket, the completed acrosome consists of two concentric cones.[60] The spermatozoon of the cockroach, on the other hand, has a prominent disc-like acrosome which is easily visible by phase-contrast microscopy.[82]

The function of the acrosome in insects remains a subject for speculation. In some other organisms, at least, it is involved in the ' acrosomal reaction ' in which substances diffusing from the eggs cause the acrosome to discharge a long filament. This filament is considered to be important in establishing the initial contact between egg and spermatozoa. Whether such a reaction occurs in insect spermatozoa is unknown, but it seems likely that the most anterior part of the cell might be specialized for establishing contact between the spermatozoon and the egg.

Almost all of the insects studied so far possess long, filamentous spermatozoa in which, by light microscopy at least, the head is but little differentiated from the tail. Certainly the head and the tail appear to be of roughly the same diameter. Many insect spermatozoa are also very long; those of *Rhodnius*, for example, are about 300 μ in length.[25] The very pronounced filamentous nature of insect spermatozoa is probably an indirect consequence of life on land. We shall see in Chapter 4 that the spermatozoa enter the egg through a micropyle in the chorion. The chorion is a waterproof covering over the egg and is, of course, an adaptation to a terrestrial habitat. If this waterproofing mechanism is to be effective, any holes in it, such as the micropyles, should be as small as possible. The small diameter of the micropyles obviously imposes an upper limit on the diameter of the spermatozoa. The eggs of the cockroach *Periplaneta americana* are protected from desiccation by a second enclosure, the ootheca. The chorion in *Periplaneta* is not particularly well-developed and the micropyles are less narrow. It is perhaps significant that the spermatozoa of *Periplaneta* resemble more closely those of other animals in that they have a distinct head.

Although some aspects of spermiogenesis are reasonably well documented for a variety of insects, we have as yet no clear picture of the submicroscopic morphology of the mature spermatozoon of any one species. From what has been done on a variety of species, however, it is possible to present a composite and hypothetical picture of an insect spermatozoon (fig. 3). Note that the mitochondrial nebenkern, which is formed from the condensation of the mitochondria of the spermatocyte, forms a sheath, or perhaps extends alongside, the axial filament throughout almost its entire length. Thus, there is, strictly speaking, no middle piece in insect spermatozoa, since this structure in other animals (for instance mammals) is composed of the helically wound mitochondria. The centriole, as mentioned earlier, gives rise to the axial filament. In most insects, as in other animals, the centriole is located directly behind the nucleus, but in *Cicindela* and *Lepisma*, the centriole migrates to a position in front of the nucleus, dragging with it the axial filament and mitochondria.[81]

The activities of the testis, then, result in the production of cysts containing spermatozoa. Normally, a large number of spermatozoa is produced before the final moult, but in some species at least, spermatogenesis continues during the adult life of the insect. The passage of the spermatozoa into the vas deferens and seminal vesicle is often a very complex process. In some Heteroptera, for instance, the developing spermatids, enclosed in their cysts, proceed towards the apex of the tubule, probably propelled by the force of elongation of the developing cells. They then turn and proceed in a spiral course to the base of the tubule where the cysts rupture and the mature spermatozoa pass into the vas deferens.[27, 93]

In these cases the force for the apparent wanderings of the developing spermatozoa is supplied by the elongation of the cell. However, in a grasshopper, *Chortophaga*, the mature spermatozoa, free of the cysts but held together by a hyaline cap over the heads of the spermatozoa, take a similar journey through the tubule. In this case it is apparently the lashing of the tails of the spermatozoa that provides the motive power.[92] How widespread such

B

phenomena are, or what the precise significance of these intratubular wanderings is, are matters which await further investigation. Nevertheless, it is tempting to speculate that the intratubular movements of the spermatozoa, which bring them near the apical cell, may be concerned with providing the spermatozoa with necessary substrates.

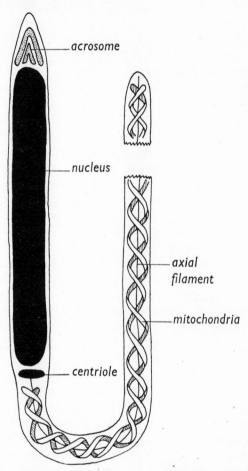

FIG. 3. Diagram representing a possible structure for the spermatozoa of insects. The mitochondria are here shown as being arranged in helices, but they may simply extend alongside the axial filament.

In other insects, the passage into the vas deferens is less complex. In *Rhodnius*, the cysts containing the mature spermatozoa pass into the short vasa efferentia, which connect the tubules with the vas deferens, by squeezing between large cells which form a plug at the base of each tubule. The cysts disappear soon after the sperms enter the vas deferens. In the scarabeid beetles and the silkworm moth, the tubules are separated from the vasa efferentia by the ' basilar membrane ', which the spermatozoa must penetrate when they pass into the vas deferens.[32, 89, 123] While there is as yet no experimental evidence, the plug of cells at the base of the seminiferous tubule in *Rhodnius* is obviously secretory and it may be that in their passage among these cells, the spermatozoa are receiving substrates necessary for their maintenance in the seminal vesicles.

In many species the heads of the spermatozoa from a single cyst are held together by a hyaline cap. This normally disappears when the spermatozoa pass into the vas deferens, but in *Chortophaga* the cap persists until after the transfer of the semen has occurred. In the mealy bugs, the spermatozoa are held in bundles by an elaborate corkscrew-shaped sheath which persists until just before the eggs are fertilized.[88]

The spermatozoa in the seminal vesicles are quiescent; movement is practically absent. In the spermathecae of the female, however, the spermatozoa are in constant and violent activity. The ' wave motion ' characteristic of active, tightly packed spermatozoa and resulting from their synchronous beating is very obvious in the spermathecae. What, then, are the reasons for such differences in the activity of mature spermatozoa? Because we know so little about the biochemistry of the semen of insects, any answers to this question are bound to be tentative.

In most insects, the spermatozoa in the seminal vesicles are very tightly packed indeed, and it might be that crowding itself is responsible for their inactivity. The spermatozoa of *Periplaneta* exhibit slightly lower tail beat frequencies at higher concentrations. Thus, at a concentration of 3000 cells per cu. mm. the frequency is about 700 beats per minute, and at 21,000 cells per cu. mm. it is about 575. This ' dilution effect ' is also said to be quite evident in semen from honey bees.[7, 25] However, differences in activity of this sort could hardly explain the differences in activity encountered in the intact animal. Even those spermatozoa near the periphery of the seminal vesicles in *Rhodnius* and *Periplaneta* beat only feebly.

In insects, oxygen is supplied to the tissues through a tracheal system. In a sac such as the seminal vesicle only the cells of the wall are tracheated and diffusion must be responsible for the transport of oxygen to the contents. The availability of oxygen could very easily be limiting under such circumstances. On the other hand, the spermatozoa of both *Periplaneta* and *Rhodnius* will exhibit activity for just as long in the absence of oxygen as when oxygen is readily available. Furthermore, the spermatozoa of *Periplaneta* under anaerobic conditions will decolourize methylene blue, thus demonstrating that anaerobiosis is indeed occurring.[25]

While the spermatozoa of some species (e.g. *Apis mellifera*) are attached by their heads to the glandular epidermis of the seminal vesicle,[5] in many species the wall of the seminal vesicle is not secretory, and it is possible that the spermatozoa are quiescent because of the relative absence of some substrate necessary for movements. However, in most insects, the spermatozoa from the seminal vesicles will exhibit activity when placed into a saline solution which does not contain substrates.

The spermatozoa of *Periplaneta* are sensitive to pH; they exhibit maximum activity at a pH of about 7·5. At higher levels of pH they are completely inactive; at lower levels they are less active. In *Rhodnius*, the pH of the environment in which the spermatozoa are found changes dramatically. In the testis, vas deferens and seminal vesicle the pH is near 7·0, but in the bulbus ejaculatorius and female reproductive tract including the spermathecae, the pH is about 5·5. When spermatozoa from within the seminal vesicle or the spermathecae are placed in a saline of pH about 5·5 they are violently active, whereas at pH 7·0 they are far less active. An unfavourable pH can be put down as one of the factors responsible for the feeble activity of the spermatozoa in the seminal vesicles of *Rhodnius*. It remains to be seen whether this observation has any general application.[22, 25]

In many insects a number of glands in the male have been said to secrete a material which activates the spermatozoa. For example, in *Bombyx mori*, part of the ejaculatory duct, referred to as the ' prostate gland ' is held to have a stimulatory effect on the spermatozoa. This activation of the spermatozoa may be quite important in this species since artificial inseminations are unsuccessful unless the secretions of the prostate are included.[91] There is no evidence to suggest how this activation takes place; the author assumes that the prostatic secretion supplies metabolites necessary for the movement of the spermatozoa. In the cockchafer, *Melolontha melolontha*, one of the components of the spermatophore appears to activate the spermatozoa,[68] but again the mode of action of the activation is a matter for speculation. Various authors have suggested that the availability of oxygen might be a limiting factor in the activity of insect spermatozoa, but evidence is accumulating that the spermatozoa of various species are active in the total absence of oxygen.[25, 68] It is clear that we know almost nothing of the metabolism of semen nor of the effects of various factors on the activity of the spermatozoa.

In the spermathecae of most insects the spermatozoa are maintained in a state of continuous activity for very long periods. In *Rhodnius* the spermatozoa in the spermathecae remain active and viable for at least a month after a single copulation[64]; in the honey bee and some ants, spermatozoa are said to survive in the female for several years.[114] Obviously some form of exogenous substrate must provide the energy necessary for the constant motion. In mammalian semen, the metabolic requirements of the spermatozoa during the relatively short time that they are active in the female ducts are provided by fructose from the seminal fluid. Insect semen has a very small component of seminal fluid as compared to spermatozoa, and on these grounds alone it is unlikely that the secretions of the accessory glands of the male would provide all of the metabolic requirements of the spermatozoa in the female. Semen from the drone bee certainly contains fructose as well as glucose and trehalose and fructolysis occurs in the semen. On the other hand, the concentration of fructose in the various parts of the male reproductive tract is not much higher than that in the blood, and drones returning from flight exhibit a very much reduced concentration of all three sugars in the reproductive organs.[7] These facts, coupled with the high rate of fructolysis in the semen, make it unlikely that any fructose which would be deposited in the queen bee by the inseminating drone would suffice to maintain the spermatozoa for more than a few minutes.

In most insects, parts of the spermathecal epithelium are obviously glandular; in many species there is a more or less distinct spermathecal gland. In *Rhodnius*, the spermathecae of virgin females contain a secretion in the lumen. This secretion has many of the properties of a lipoprotein and it may be that it forms the source of exogenous substrate for the spermatozoa. This is not to suggest that a lipoprotein enters into the intracellular metabolism of the spermatozoa; it is far more likely that the lipoprotein would be digested extracellularly and a simple molecule would be utilized by the spermatozoa.[25]

3: The Female System and the Eggs

It is the task of the female reproductive system to receive and store the products of the male system, to produce the eggs, to ensure that the eggs and the spermatozoa meet and to deposit the eggs. In this chapter we shall be concerned mainly with the process of oogenesis or egg-production; the phenomena of copulation, fertilization and oviposition will be discussed in later chapters.

The internal organs of reproduction in female insects vary from species to species (fig. 4). In general, however, there is a pair of mesodermal ovaries, each of which opens into a lateral oviduct. The two lateral oviducts unite to form a single median, usually heavily muscular, common oviduct. The bursa copulatrix, when present, is the vagina of the insect; it receives the copulatory apparatus of the male. Commonly, the bursa is simply a posterior, sac-like enlargement of the common oviduct but in the Lepidoptera it has become almost completely separated from the rest of the system. The spermatheca, which is the storage organ of the spermatozoa received during copulation, is most often a single diverticulum of the bursa or common oviduct. The paired spermathecae of *Rhodnius* are not homologous with the spermathecae of other Heteroptera. The homologous structure in *Rhodnius* is the single cement gland opening from the bursa. The spermatheca has a secretory epithelium presumably supplying nutrient for the spermatozoa which are stored there and, in many insects, one portion of the spermatheca may be specialized as the spermathecal gland.   The secretory cells are often provided with intracellular ductules.

Various accessory glands may also be present: these are normally associated with the formation of egg-cases or cements

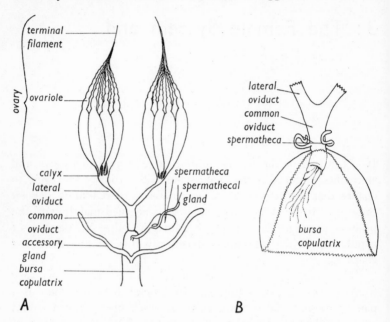

FIG. 4.   *A*. Female organs of a ' typical ' insect (after Snodgrass).   *B*. Ventral view of the female ducts of *Rhodnius*, with the bursa copulatrix opened to reveal the entrance to the common oviduct.

used in fastening the eggs to the substratum.   The bursa copulatrix, the spermathecae and the common oviduct are normally lined with a chitinous intima, thus indicating their ectodermal origin.   The lateral oviducts are normally mesodermal in origin but in a number of species they too may be lined with cuticle.

Each ovary consists of a number of tubules or ovarioles enclosed in a common membrane, the outer epithelial sheath, composed of epithelial cells, connective tissue and a number of branching muscle cells which form a diffuse network in the active ovary. The ovary is very well supplied with tracheae. The number of ovarioles in each ovary is characteristic of the species. In *Periplaneta*, for example, there are eight; in Lepidoptera there are normally four and in a few species, notably the viviparous Diptera which produce relatively few eggs, there may be only one ovariole per ovary. Many insects have a very much larger number of ovarioles; in the Isoptera the number on each side may be in excess of 2000.[55] The ovary is attached to the dorsal diaphragm by the suspensory ligament, a slender structure made up of the terminal filaments of the various ovarioles.

The ovariole is the functional unit of the ovary and consists of the terminal filament, germarium, vitellarium and pedicel. The germarium, vitellarium and pedicel form a tube bounded by a simple epithelial sheath. In the germarium, mitotic activity gives rise to primary oocytes which enter the vitellarium along with their associated follicle cells. During their progress along the vitellarium they grow as a result of the deposition of yolk, a process known as vitellogenesis. At the posterior end of the vitellarium, the mature oocyte enters the pedicel of the ovariole and is ultimately discharged into the lateral oviduct during the process of ovulation which is discussed elsewhere. Vitellogenesis is a period of intense growth. In *Drosophila*, for instance, the oocyte increases in volume by 10^5 in three days,[66] and in the Cecropia silk moth the increment has been calculated to be 91 per cent. per day for a period of five weeks.[116]

The precise manner by which vitellogenesis proceeds depends to a considerable extent on which type of ovariole is involved. Three types are recognized (fig. 5). The **panoistic ovariole** is one in which specialized nutritive cells are lacking. The germarium contains oogonia which give rise by mitosis to young oocytes near the posterior end of the germarium. The oogonia and oocytes are surrounded by a mass of prefollicular tissue which is particularly abundant near the posterior part of the germarium. As the young oocytes move into the vitellarium, they are surrounded by prefollicular nuclei between which cell membranes appear so that the oocyte is completely enveloped in a follicular epithelium. The oocyte with its surrounding layer of follicular epithelium comprises the follicle. Each follicle is separated from the follicles immediately anterior and posterior to it by a plug of modified follicular cells, the interfollicular tissue. Panoistic

ovarioles are characteristic of the older orders of insects—the
Thysanura, Orthoptera, Isoptera, Odonata and Plecoptera. The

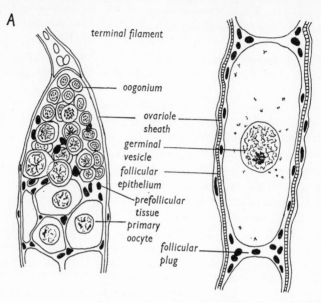

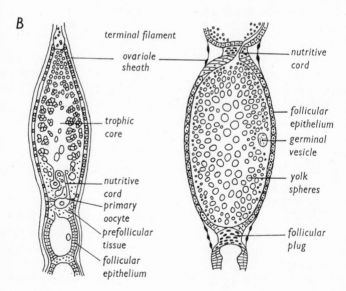

Siphonaptera is the only holometabolous order which possesses panoistic ovarioles.[11]

The **telotrophic ovary** (sometimes referred to as **acrotrophic**) and the **polytrophic ovary** possess, in addition to the structures already described, large nurse cells, or trophocytes, which are important in the production of yolk. These two types together are sometimes referred to as **meroistic ovaries**.

Telotrophic ovaries are characteristic of the Hemiptera and some Coleoptera. The Heteropteran ovary has been abundantly studied, and the following account is based on some of this work.[8, 9, 11] The most anterior part of the germarium contains undifferentiated cells in the process of proliferation. Immediately behind this, mitosis is absent and groups of nuclei cluster together. Cell boundaries disappear. The nuclei fuse, so that there is a progressive increase in size of nuclei. These nuclei comprise the differentiating trophocytes.

Further back in the germarium, the clusters of trophic nuclei

FIG. 5. Germarium (left) and a maturing follicle (right) in : *A*, a panoistic ovary; *B*, a telotrophic ovary; and *C*, a polytrophic ovary. (Modified after Bonhag and King, Robinson and Smith.)

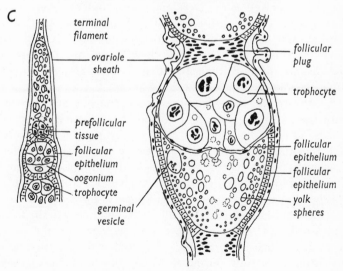

C

terminal
filament

ovariole
sheath

follicular
plug

trophocyte

prefollicular
tissue

follicular
epithelium

oogonium

trophocyte

follicular
epithelium

follicular
epithelium

yolk
spheres

germinal
vesicle

arrange themselves about a central core of cytoplasm, the trophic core, which is continuous with the cytoplasm in which the clusters of trophic nuclei are situated. This area, then, is a syncytium with a peripheral concentration of nuclei. There is a continuous movement of these giant nuclei into the trophic core, where they disintegrate. The nuclei expended in this way are replaced by mitoses in the most anterior part of the germarium, followed by fusion of nuclei. Cords of cytoplasm, the trophic cords, extend from the trophic core to the developing oocyte. Each of these nutritive cords remains attached to its particular oocyte throughout the course of its development.

The oocytes themselves are produced from the oogonia, a disc of germ cells just posterior to the trophic core. The young oocytes produced by the mitotoc activity of the oogonia become surrounded by prefollicular tissue as described for the panoistic ovariole. The young oocyte, surrounded by its prefollicular nuclei and attached to the trophic core by its nutritive cord, enters the vitellarium where vitellogenesis occurs. In the telotrophic ovary of *Tenebrio*, the trophic tissue retains its cellular character.[104]

The nurse cells in the **polytrophic ovariole**, on the other hand, are enclosed in the follicle with the developing oocyte. Polytrophic ovaries are characteristic of most of the holometabolous orders, as well as the Dermaptera, Psocoptera, Anoplura and Mallophaga. Although the ovarioles of the Dermaptera are the simplest case in that only one trophocyte appears with each oocyte,[10, 11] those of *Drosophila* have been more extensively studied and are more typical in that they possess a number of trophocytes in each follicle.[65, 66]

In *Drosophila*, there are about 50 mitotically active oogonia in the apex of each germarium. When one of these germinal cells divides, one of the daughter cells simply repeats the process, while the other oogonium undergoes four consecutive synchronous divisions to produce a cyst of 16 cells. This cyst of cells becomes surrounded by prefollicular tissue and moves out of the germarium into the vitellarium where a typical follicle is formed.

At first the rate of growth of all 16 daughter cells in the follicle is identical, but ultimately the most posterior cell, the oocyte, grows very much more rapidly. Eventually the 15 trophocytes will shrink, especially during the later phases of vitellogenesis, and will ultimately be resorbed. During vitellogenesis the oocyte becomes gradually cut off from the trophocytes by a layer of follicle cells, although earlier the cytoplasm of the oocyte is confluent with that of adjacent trophocytes by means of minute pores (about $0 \cdot 5 \ \mu$) in the cell membranes.

In the insect egg, the cytoplasm is not often conspicuous. A layer of cortical cytoplasm or periplasm is usually visible at the periphery of the egg; the rest of the cytoplasm occurs as a scanty reticulum. Most of the egg is taken up with the yolk or deutoplasm, which is almost entirely comprised of two sorts of spherical bodies. The protein yolk bodies are the most abundant. Each protein body is enclosed in a delicate membrane and contains some carbohydrate, indicative perhaps of a mucin.[117] The lipid yolk bodies have been intensively studied in a number of insects.[11, 79, 80] Early in vitellogenesis, phospholipids are most abundant but later the phospholipids decrease in concentration and triglycerides become apparent. Many insects also deposit glycogen during vitellogenesis.[10]

The origin of the protein yolk spheres has been associated with bodies which are extruded from the nucleolus of the oocyte and which eventually pass into the cytoplasm. Thus there are many reports in the older literature describing these nucleolar emission bodies. In most cases the bodies are held to fragment, migrate to the periphery of the oocyte and grow into the typical yolk spheres. However, it has been pointed out[11] that such a hypothesis is based on the observation that the nucleolus extrudes bodies and that similar bodies can later be seen at the periphery of the oocyte. These latter bodies then grow into the protein spheres. It is true that studies with the electron microscope have revealed that trophocyte nuclei extrude material in *Rhodnius* and *Drosophila*, but this material appears to break down before it reaches the oocyte.[65] It is tempting to relate these extrusion bodies to the nucleic acid which is so often associated with vitellogenesis.

Since nucleic acids are constantly associated with the synthesis of protein, observations on DNA and RNA in the developing oocyte and its associated tissues are relevant to the discussion of the protein bodies. In insects with meroistic ovarioles, there is abundant evidence that the trophocytes contribute DNA in substantial quantities to the developing oocytes. In *Oncopeltus*, for example,[8] trophocyte nuclei pass into the central cytoplasmic core of the apical nurse tissue, migrate to the posterior end of the trophic core and become pycnotic. These degenerating nuclei release droplets of DNA, which then break down and are presumably transported to the oocyte along the nutritive cord to be utilized in the synthesis of nucleic acids. The trophocytes of *Oncopeltus* also appear to contribute some of the proteinaceous elements to the oocytes as protein. The evidence also suggests that the oocyte nucleus itself may be involved in the synthesis of protein during vitellogenesis. In young oocytes there is abundant RNA to be found around the nucleus and at least one of the several nucleoli is very large and is associated with a mass of DNA. Furthermore, there is a high concentration of protein near the nucleus of these young oocytes. Thus, these and other studies on the nucleic acids of the ovariole suggest that the oocyte synthesizes a good deal of the protein which makes up the deutoplasm and that much of the nucleic acid necessary for this synthesis is contributed by the trophocytes. In *Tenebrio* the young oocytes are rich in RNA.[104] In panoistic ovaries, of course, the nucleic acids would have to be contributed by either the oocyte nucleus or the follicle cells. In *Schistocerca*, RNA is present in large amounts in the follicle cells during vitellogenesis.[75]

That the follicle cells play an important rôle in the development of the proteinaceous elements in yolk has been revealed by the elegant researches of Telfer and his colleagues[115-119] into vitellogenesis in Saturniid moths. They have demonstrated that two proteins, antigen 3, a carotenoid protein, and antigen 7, the 'female protein', occur in the blood of females in considerable amounts until vitellogenesis begins, when they are accumulated in the developing oocytes. In the case of antigen 7, the protein has been shown to enter the oocyte unchanged via the follicle cells and not the trophocytes, the entry being facilitated by the presence of a brush border on the oocyte. Antigen 7 is localized in the protein bodies and is accumulated to twenty times the concentration at which it occurs in the blood. In the locust, a high concentration of protein in the blood has been associated with vitellogenesis. At the same time as the protein increases, the concentration of free amino acids in the haemolymph decreases, suggesting perhaps that the amino acids, which are particularly abundant in insect haemolymph, act as a pool for protein synthesis.

The earlier workers were generally agreed that the lipid bodies arose from the Golgi apparatus. However, at that time, the precise nature and distribution of the Golgi material were matters of some dispute, so that it would be unwise to associate the lipid bodies with the Golgi apparatus until relevant studies with the electron microscope are forthcoming. Nevertheless it is clear that precursors of the lipid bodies appear first near one pole of the nucleus of the oocyte while it is still in the germarium. These granules become more numerous, grow in size and spread throughout the deutoplasm. In panoistic ovaries, as are found in the cockroach, the precursors of the lipid bodies spread to the periphery of the oocyte where they grow as a result of accumulation of materials transported into the oocyte by the follicle cells.[80] In Heteroptera, which have telotrophic ovarioles, the precursors to the lipid bodies apparently receive lipids from the trophocytes during their early development, but later most of the precursors derive their lipids from the follicle cells.[9] In the polytrophic follicles of *Culex*, the nurse cells do not appear to contribute to lipogenesis.[79] Thus it appears to be the follicle cells which are most important in the transport of lipids into the developing oocyte. The lipid bodies are at first composed mainly of lipoproteins, especially phospholipids. As development proceeds, however, the protein component becomes less and less apparent, until in the mature egg most of the lipid occurs without associated protein.

Glycogen occurs in the yolks of some, but not all, insect eggs. Normally it appears later in vitellogenesis after the trophocytes have degenerated; in these cases it probably enters the egg through the follicle cells. In the earwig *Anisolabis*, the glycogen is contributed to the oocyte by the single trophocyte in each follicle.[10]

The sites at which the various materials passed into the oocyte are elaborated is a matter for conjecture. Certainly the fat body undergoes cyclical changes associated with cycles of egg development. Adult Lepidoptera are unable to assimilate protein, and the proteinaceous elements of the eggs must be derived from reserves laid down by the larva. As eggs develop in the

Lepidoptera the size of the fat body diminishes. There is abundant evidence that nutrition affects vitellogenesis.[129]

Many insects possess symbiotic micro-organisms which are essential to their exploitation of various materials as food. There is a variety of mechanisms by which newly hatched young are infected with their symbionts, but frequently the micro-organisms find their way into the developing oocytes. The route of entry into the egg is usually via the follicle cells. Thus, in *Blatta*, the bacterial symbionts invade the follicle cells from which they move to the peripheral oöplasm. Here they become encapsulated in a system of membranes and eventually find their way to the poles of the mature egg.[39] The invasion of the follicle cells probably occurs from the mycetocytes which are scattered through the fat body.

The developing oocyte now has its total complement of yolk, which is the food supply for the embryo which will develop after fertilization. But the egg is not yet complete: it must be provided with a protective coating. The properties required of such a protective coating are that it should permit the exchange of gases necessary for the respiration of the embryo and that it should protect the embryo from desiccation. Furthermore, since fertilization normally occurs after the shell has been formed, some means must exist for the entry of the spermatozoa.

Some insects, of course, notably among the Orthopteroid orders, place the eggs in groups in a protective coating or ootheca the formation of which is discussed elsewhere. Here we are concerned only with the formation of the egg shell or chorion. The oocyte itself is contained in the vitelline membrane, which is believed by some authors[2, 129] to consist simply of the modified plasma membrane of the oocyte. In *Drosophila*, however, evidence from the electron microscope[65] makes it quite clear that the vitelline membrane forms as a condensation of droplets secreted by the follicle cells.

It is generally agreed that the chorion is the product of the follicle cells. In panoistic ovarioles, of course, the follicle cells completely surround the developing oocyte but in meroistic ovarioles it is discontinuous at the point of entry of the nutritive cord or in the area around the pore which connects the trophocytes with the oocyte. In the final stages of oogenesis, however, the follicle cells completely surround the oocyte and in the case of polytrophic ovarioles, the nurse cells associated with the follicle degenerate.

There are normally two layers distinguishable in the chorion of most insect eggs: the endochorion next to the vitelline membrane and the exochorion. McFARLANE[77] has pointed out that the insect chorion conforms to the concept of a cuticle with a thin lipoprotein layer, the epicuticle, which in the case of the chorion is next to the vitelline membrane and a thick inner proteinaceous layer, the endocuticle. Note that while this is a cuticle which is inside out with respect to the egg, these layers are in the proper order with respect to the cells which secrete them, the follicle cells. McFARLANE therefore refers to the chorion as the maternal cuticle; the endochorion (lipoprotein) then becomes the maternal epicuticle and the exochorion (protein) becomes the maternal endocuticle. This argument has much to recommend it but one of the corollaries of such a system is the fact that the follicular cells, which are mesodermal, are held to secrete a cuticle, a function which is normally assigned to ectoderm.

There may be elaborations on this basic pattern of chorionic structure. In *Rhodnius*, for example, it is possible to distinguish a total of seven subdivisions of the two major layers.[2] The first sign of secretion of the chorion in *Rhodnius* is the appearance on the vitelline membrane of droplets of material having the properties of a polyphenol. This, the inner polyphenol layer, is discontinuous and takes the form of islands of the droplets over the surface of the vitelline membrane. The follicle cells next secrete a tanned proteinaceous layer which is very resistant to various reagents; it is therefore termed the resistant protein layer. The outer polyphenol layer, like the inner one consists of discontinuous groups of droplets arranged in islands. This layer of droplets acts as a substratum for the secretion of the so-called ' amber-layer '; its presence elsewhere can only be inferred from experimental evidence. The outermost of the five layers of the endochorion consists of a less resistant layer of protein, termed the soft endochorion. The exochorion is secreted as two layers: the soft exochorion, which is probably a lipoprotein, and the resistant exochorion, the thin but tough outermost layer of the egg. The exochorion is secreted much more rapidly at the periphery of

C

the follicle cells than at the centre.   This results in the formation of follicular pits at intervals over the surface of the shell; the characteristic sculpturing of the surface of the egg in *Rhodnius* is completed by the persistence on the surface of the polygonal outlines of the follicle cells.   During the secretion of the exochorion, the pits are filled by projections from the follicle cells.

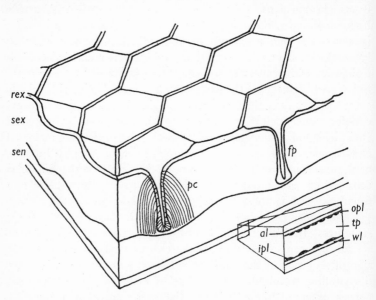

FIG. 6.   Diagram of the layers found in the egg of *Rhodnius*
(after Beament).

al, amber layer; *fp*, follicular pit; *ipl*, inner polyphenol layer; *opl*, outer polyphenol layer; *pc*, pore canals; *rex*, resistant exochorion; *sen*, soft endochorion; *sex*, soft exochorion; *tp*, tanned protein layer; *wl*, wax layer.

From these villi small pore canals radiate into the exochorion (fig. 6).   In acridid eggs, in addition to the two layers of the maternal cuticle, an inner wax layer, said to be associated with the vitelline membrane, and an outer ' extrachorion ' are present.[43]

In most insects the spermatozoa enter the egg by passing along the micropyles, which are narrow channels, usually much twisted, through all of the layers of the chorion.   In *Rhodnius* they number 10-20 and are confined to the spermatic groove, an annular indentation in the shell at its anterior end. The micropyle is apparently produced by follicle cells with very much larger villi.[4] The number and the position of the micropyles in the eggs of other insects vary from species to species. Most Diptera, for instance, have only a single micropyle and in *Locusta* the number varies from 35 to 43.[129]

The eggs of many species are highly resistant to desiccation. In *Rhodnius*, there is no loss of water to a dry atmosphere from intact eggs at temperatures up to $42 \cdot 5^\circ$ C.; above this ' critical temperature ' the rate of desiccation increases sharply. This phenomenon is held to be due to the disruption of an extremely thin layer of wax, the presence of which can only be inferred from indirect experimental evidence.[3] Since the egg of *Rhodnius* is impermeable for a short time after the chorion is complete, the wax layer is probably secreted by the oocyte itself. How far these observations may be extended to other groups of insects is uncertain. As we have noted earlier, the eggs of acridids have a wax layer associated with the vitelline membrane. A layer of grease or wax seems to be present on the inner surfaces of the eggs of *Dixippus*,[131] *Lucilia*,[26] *Melanoplus*[107] and a variety of other species. Whether or not these layers are primarily responsible for the waterproofing of the egg is another matter. In the orthopteroid orders, the embryo often takes up water from the environment. In *Acheta*, the period of water absorption corresponds with the disintegration of the maternal epicuticle and it is reasonable to conclude that this layer is the barrier to water.[78] Similarly, in various acridids, it is the disintegration of the ' extrachorion ' which signals water absorption.[43] In many insects, particularly among the Orthoptera, the absorption of water is the particular function of a specialized area of the shell and underlying embryonic tissues; these areas are sometimes called ' hydropyles '.

It is not easy to see at first sight how chorions like those which cover most insect oocytes permit the passage of the gases necessary for the development of the embryo. It is true that the micropyles pierce the chorion but these are often occluded by accessory secretions from the female. The aeropyles open onto the surface of the egg but they are few in number and do not penetrate the lower layers of the chorion. In *Rhodnius*, the site of gaseous exchange is the rim of the cap on the anterior end of the egg, an area which includes the aeropyles. It is necessary on theoretical grounds for these aeropyles to communicate with a continuous air space near the surface of the oocyte.[122] The precise nature of this space has been somewhat elusive, but recent investigations employing both light and electron microscopy on a variety of species have shown that the following scheme is probably generally applicable.[51-53, 131, 132]

In most insects the aeropyles connect with a gas-filled meshwork which is separated from the vitelline membrane by only a thin layer of the chorion. This gas-filled meshwork forms the continuous gas layer which it was necessary to postulate for gas exchange to take place. The connection between this layer and the atmosphere is accomplished in a variety of ways. In *Rhodnius* the aeropyles at the rim of the cap form the only connection. The

FIG. 7.   Respiratory structures found in insect eggs (after Hinton). *A*. Section through chorion of *Ranatra linearis* to show aeropyle. *B*. Respiratory horn of *Nepa*. *C*. Section through distal portion of *B*. *D*. Section through proximal portion of *B*.

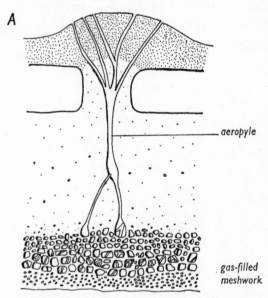

A

aeropyle

gas-filled meshwork

quatic Heteroptera have, in addition to a number of aeropyles, ne to several respiratory horns, which usually project from the vater. These long extensions of the chorion, usually at the nterior pole of the egg, have a central gas-filled meshwork which

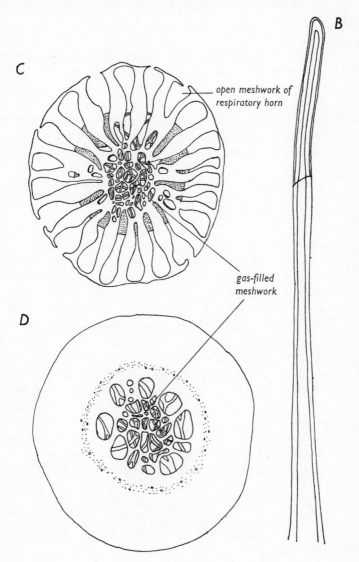

open meshwork of respiratory horn

gas-filled meshwork

is connected to the atmosphere at the distal end of the horn and is continuous with the inner gas-filled layer of the chorion. The connection to the atmosphere takes the form of a peripheral meshwork consisting of struts or rods running radially in the horn. These struts are branched at the surface of the horn so that the branches form a fine open meshwork. The surfaces of the mesh-work are hydrofuge; this prevents flooding of the gas-filled cavity when the egg is immersed. Many dipterous eggs have a similar arrangement. Here two parallel folds of the chorion enclose between them the respiratory groove which runs longi-tudinally along the surface of the egg. The floor and inner walls of this groove form an open meshwork similar to the plastron on the distal end of the respiratory horns of Heteroptera and com-municate with the gas-filled network in the deeper layers of the chorion (fig. 7).

The advantages of such a system lie in the fact that while a relatively large surface of gas is in contact with the inner layers of the shell, this gas volume communicates with the atmosphere through a relatively small cross-section. Furthermore, the hydrofuge elements of the open meshwork on the outer surface of the respiratory horns of aquatic Heteroptera and the respiratory groove in the eggs of Diptera permit the formation of a plastron for the efficient exchange of gases when the egg is submerged.[51]

In certain circumstances, which are not at all clearly under-stood, the process of egg production in the ovaries may be reversed and the oocytes resorbed. In the desert locust, resorption of a terminal oocyte in any ovariole may begin at any stage of vitel-logenesis short of maturity. During resorption the follicle cells, which in this panoistic ovary are responsible for the transfer of all of the nutrients into the oocyte, reverse their rôle and become vitellophages. They secrete enzymes which digest the yolk, putting it into a form suitable for resorption. The degenerating oocyte shrinks, the follicle cells invade the yolk, and, as first the protein and later the lipid become completely digested, the follicle cells themselves degenerate, leaving a transitory and functionless mass.[75] The conditions which bring about or accelerate the pro-cess of resorption have not been fully explored; we shall see in a later chapter that the process is under the influence of the endocrine system.

4 : The Transfer of Semen

As we saw in Chapter 1, one of the prerequisites for life on land is the provision of some means for the internal fertilization of the egg. This implies a form of copulation, during which semen from the seminal vesicles of the male is transferred to the female. In most insects the semen must be transported to a spermatheca, where it is stored until it is used to fertilize the eggs just before they are laid.

In order to understand the various mechanisms by which the transfer of semen is effected, it is necessary to examine the morphology of the external genitalia of the male. It is as well to admit at the outset that the subject is confused. The external genitalia of insects vary so widely from species to species that they are often used as diagnostic characters by taxonomists. Unfortunately, this very multiformity which has so delighted the taxonomist induces a melancholic gloom in the student of physiology.

The nomenclature of the various parts of the genitalia varies from order to order and from author to author, and there have been relatively few attempts to homologize the structures in the various orders. As a consequence it is important to realize that any attempt at a general scheme is bound to be somewhat arbitrary. In this book we shall follow SNODGRASS[110] who has attempted to interpret the genitalia of male insects on the basis of their embryology.

In insects, the male genitalia are derived from a pair of small ectodermal outgrowths on the ventral surface of the posterior end of the ninth segment in the nymph or larva. These are the primary phallic lobes which in the Ephemeroptera form the two penes.

In the Thysanura the two primary lobes unite to form a single median penis. In all of the other orders each primary lobe divides longitudinally to form a medial mesomere and lateral paramere.

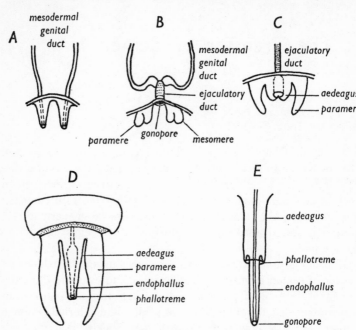

FIG. 8. Diagrams representing the development of, and some of the variations in, the external genitalia of male insects (after Snodgrass). *A.* The condition in Ephemeroptera, showing paired penes. *B.* Differentiation of the primary phallic lobes into mesomeres and parameres surrounding a single gonopore. *C.* The mesomeres fuse to form the aedeagus. *D.* Aedeagus, with parameres forming claspers. *E.* Aedeagus with endophallus everted out through phallotreme, making the gonopore the terminal opening.

The ejaculatory duct arises as an ectodermal ingrowth between the bases of the mesomeres and forms a connection with the vasa deferentia and the ducts of the accessory glands. In the Orthoptera the subsequent development of the mesomeres and parameres is complex, but in the higher orders the two mesomeres unite to form a hollow tube, the aedeagus. The lumen of the

aedeagus is thus an extension of the ejaculatory duct and is termed
the endophallus.   The junction between the endophallus and
the ejaculatory duct is the gonopore, and the distal opening of the
endophallus is the phallotreme.   The system may be arranged so
that the endophallus is everted out through the phallotreme
thereby rendering the gonopore the effective terminal opening.
The two parameres develop into the clasping organs of the adult
insect.   These various relationships are illustrated in the diagrams
in figure 8.

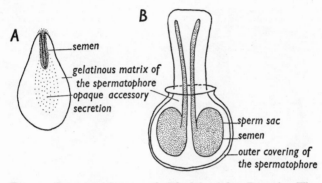

FIG. 9.   Spermatophores.   *A. Rhodnius* (after Davey).   The
anterior slit, containing the semen, encloses the entrance to
the common oviduct shown in figure 4*B*.   *B*. A more typical
spermatophore from a Neuropteran (after Khalifa).   The
neck of the spermatophore extends into the female ducts,
while the bulb may protrude from the genital opening.

It is obviously beyond the scope of this book to consider in
detail the process of copulation in all of the species which have been
examined.   Our purpose will be better served by examining only
two species, each of which represents one of the two broad cate-
gories of insemination in insects.   *Rhodnius prolixus*, a large blood-
sucking Heteropteran, transfers a spermatophore containing the
semen to the bursa copulatrix of the female.   The spermatophore
is a roughly pear-shaped mass of transparent jelly with a slit
containing the semen in the narrow portion of the mass.   On the
same surface, but on the broader part of the spermatophore, is a
slightly opaque area (fig. 9).

The spermatophore is wholly a product of the male.   The

transparent jelly forming most of the structure originates in the transparent accessory glands and is probably a mucoprotein. Its transformation from the liquid material in the lumen of the gland to the jelly of the spermatophore is a consequence of the changes in pH which, as we have seen in Chapter 2, occur along the length of the male system. Thus, in the glands themselves, where the pH is about 7, the secretion is liquid, but at the level of the bulbus ejaculatorius and intromittent organ, the pH changes abruptly to about 5·5 which is the iso-electric point of the secretion.

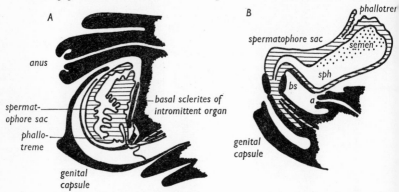

FIG. 10. Diagrams of median longitudinal sections through the genital capsule of *Rhodnius*. *A*, normal. *B*, everted as during the formation of the spermatophore.

bs, basal sclerites of intromittent organ; *sph*, spermatophore; *a*, anus.

The spermatophore is formed within the intromittent organ of the male during copulation. As in many Heteroptera, the copulatory organs are enclosed within a genital capsule, the floor of which is a heavily sclerotized cup, probably the remains of the ninth sternite, and which is enclosed dorsally by the anal segments. A pair of claspers, the parameres, are attached to the dorso-lateral borders of the capsule. The penis in *Rhodnius* consists of a series of sclerites enclosing the much-folded spermatophore sac which is everted out through the sclerites during copulation. The spermatophore sac is composed of the aedeagus and endophallus which have become folded in on themselves as shown in figures 10 and 11. Even after eversion of the spermatophore sac, the phallotreme remains the terminal opening and the gonopore connects the intromittent organ to the ejaculatory duct.

During copulation, the ventral surfaces of the insects are in contact, so that the genital capsule with its associated structures must rotate through almost 180 degrees. The intromittent organ is inserted into the bursa copulatrix and as the secretions of the transparent accessory glands of the male fill the spermatophore sac, it is everted into the bursa. When, after about twenty

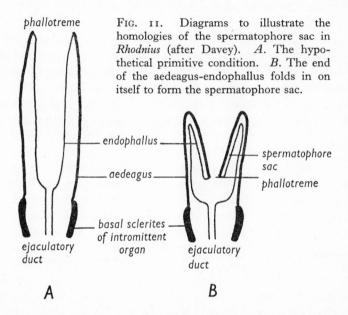

FIG. 11. Diagrams to illustrate the homologies of the spermatophore sac in *Rhodnius* (after Davey). *A*. The hypothetical primitive condition. *B*. The end of the aedeagus-endophallus folds in on itself to form the spermatophore sac.

minutes, the spermatophore within the fully everted spermatophore sac is completely formed, it is extruded from the intromittent organ which then returns to its folded condition. After a further ten minutes the intromittent organ is withdrawn, leaving the spermatophore in the bursa copulatrix. After about eight hours the spermatophore is ejected from the female and falls to the ground.[22]

Once the spermatozoa contained in the spermatophore are deposited in the bursa, they must be transported to the spermathecae, where they are stored until they are used to fertilize the eggs. We saw earlier that the spermathecae in *Rhodnius* are a

pair of diverticula opening from the common oviduct. The spermatozoa take no active part in this migration; they are transported
entirely by contractions of the oviducts set up by the presence in
the bursa of the opaque accessory secretion from the male. This
secretion is incorporated into the spermatophore so as to make
contact with the dorsal part of the bursa and thus stimulate a
peripheral nervous system. This stimulation brings about
rhythmic contractions of the oviduct and bursa which move the
spermatozoa into the spermathecae.[21]

The milkweed bug, *Oncopeltus fasciatus*, although fairly closely
related to *Rhodnius*, employs a totally different mechanism for
transferring the semen. Instead of depositing a spermatophore
within the bursa, the male *Oncopeltus* deposits the semen directly
into the single spermatheca (homologous to the cement gland in
the female of *Rhodnius*) by means of an extremely long intromittent organ. This structure is normally carried coiled up within
the genital capsule but during copulation it becomes distended
with the erection fluid which is pumped into the organ from the
erection fluid reservoir by the action of the erection fluid pump.
As a result of the increased pressure, the structure uncoils and
its tip enters the spermatheca.[12] Figure 12 is a diagram which
illustrates the relationship of the various parts in *Oncopeltus*.

The homologies of the various structures are not immediately
apparent. A possible interpretation is that the erection fluid
reservoir represents the fused bulbi; certainly the morphological
similarity is striking. Other explanations are possible with the
evidence at present available. The situation serves to emphasize
the variation in structure which is a feature of the male intromittent organ. Other insects, notably some Coleoptera, possess a
long, threadlike organ, but these are of the type described in
figure 8 and are probably erected by increased blood pressure,
brought about by the sudden contraction of the particularly
strong muscles of the abdomen and assisted by the expansion of
air sacs.

The relationships between spermatophore-producing insects
like *Rhodnius* and those which utilize a more direct method of
transfer of semen are also of interest. In general, those insects
which do not produce a spermatophore possess a more-or-less
elongated penis which penetrates during copulation to, or near,

he spermatheca.   It is clear that the transfer of semen by means
of a spermatophore represents the primitive condition.   Among
he more primitive orders such as the Thysanura or the Orthop-
eroid orders, spermatophore production is the normal method of
ransferring the semen.   Furthermore, the accessory glands of
he male which contribute to the formation of the spermatophore
are also present, often in a reduced form, in those insects which

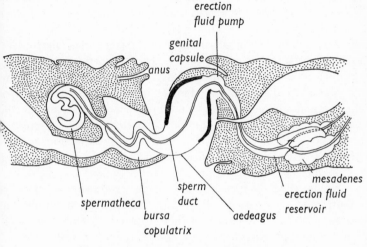

FIG. 12.   Diagram to show the relationship of the
parts in a copulating pair of *Oncopeltus* (modified
after Bonhag and Wick).

lo not produce a spermatophore.   In *Oncopeltus*, for instance, the
apparently functionless mesadenes contain a transparent secretion
with many of the properties of the transparent secretion which
orms the spermatophore in *Rhodnius*.[25]

In *Rhodnius* the spermatophore evidently functions simply as
a plug to hold the semen in place while it is being transported to
he spermatheca by the action of the muscles of the oviducts.   A
similar function probably applies for the spermatophores of some
other species, like the honey bee, where a plug formed of mucus
secreted by the male, and often parts of the external genitalia
of the male, occludes the bursa of the queen for some hours after
he nuptial flight.[6]   In the majority of spermatophore-forming

species, however, the spermatophore is a much more comple:
structure, suggesting perhaps a more complicated rôle in th
reproductive process. Typically, especially among the orthop
teroid orders, it consists of a number of membranous sperm sac
embedded in a gelatinous matrix, which often has the shape of ;
flask (fig. 9B). Among the phasmids and mantids, the bulb of the
flask remains outside the female genitalia while the long narrov
neck penetrates into the female ducts. This exposure of part o:
the spermatophore represents a hazard; female mantids are knowr
to eat the spermatophore and ants have been observed to carry of
the spermatophores of phasmids.[71, 99] Among the Dictyoptera
the ventral sclerites of the female are modified to enclose the
spermatophore and it may be that the primitive function o:
the bursa copulatrix of the female involved the protection o:
the spermatophore.   Among the other orthopteroid insects, the
Acridiids possess a much modified spermatophore. Here the
gelatinous matrix is entirely lacking and a long tubular sperm sac
which is inserted directly into the spermatheca, functions as ;
temporary extension of the intromittent organ.

Among the higher orders there is less regularity in the distribution of spermatophores. Even closely related families ir
the same order may differ in their method of semen transfer.
The panorpoid complex is a good example of this apparent
complexity. The Mecoptera are entirely without spermatophores,
although they possess reduced accessory glands, indicating that
their ancestors probably formed spermatophores. The females
of this order possess extremely long ducts leading to the spermatheca and the male genitalia of the various families show a
gradation from a sac-like penis to a long flagellum which penetrates
into the spermatheca. The Diptera are close relatives of the
Mecoptera, but reliable information on the production of spermatophores is not plentiful. All of those Diptera which have been
reported to form spermatophores are members of the Nematocera, and it is certain that some, at least, of the Cyclorrapha
deposit free sperm in the bursa. It has been suggested that all of
the Lepidoptera produce spermatophores. In the relatively few
cases which have been examined in detail, the spermatophore
consists of one to several sperm sacs embedded in a gelatinous
matrix. This spermatophore is placed in the bursa of the female

where it remains until the rather complex migration of the spermatozoa (see below) has taken place. The related Trichoptera
present a less uniform appearance. One group of families possesses
well-developed accessory glands and forms spermatophores, a
second group deposits free semen in the female and has reduced
accessory glands. The members of the remaining panorpoid
order, the Neuroptera, have retained the spermatophore in a fairly
primitive form in every family except the Coniopterygidae which
has lost the spermatophore and possesses a longer intromittent
organ.[23, 85, 86]

The semen of many insects is completely enclosed by the
spermatophore; it is therefore essential that some portion of the
spermatophore be damaged before the spermatozoa can escape.
In Lepidoptera, spines on the cuticular lining of the bursa (the
signa or cornuti of many authors) are probably responsible for
tearing open the spermatophore.[54] In other orders the problem
has not received much attention but proteolytic secretions might
cause the necessary local damage.

The origin of spermatophores has been connected by some
authors with the emergence of the aquatic ancestor of the insects
on to dry land. According to this hypothesis, the condition in
the Onychophoran *Peripatopsis*, in which the spermatophores are
placed on the body surface and the spermatozoa pass through the
cuticle into the haemocoel[76] represents a crude attempt to achieve
internal fertilization and is an early step in the development of
the modern spermatophore habit. Other Onychophora, however,
produce spermatophores which are inserted into the female
genital opening, and one group has lost the spermatophore habit,
developing instead a long flagellum-like intromittent organ. In
view of this, it is perhaps more likely that the hypothetical aquatic
ancestor of the insects, resembling perhaps the Onychophora,
already possessed a spermatophore. In this case the spermatophore may have been placed on the surface of the female near the
genital opening and may have functioned as a storage organ until
the spermatozoa were released into the water with the eggs. The
fact that some aquatic Crustacea produce a spermatophore which
functions in this way lends support to this notion. The emergence
on to land was marked not by the development of an entirely new
structure but by the modification of an existing one. The

modification would consist simply of the extension of the spermatophore into the genital opening of the female. In some cases,
as we have seen, the spermatophore has been lost and a long
intromittent organ has developed but in other cases the spermatophore has been retained, sometimes in a considerably modified
form.[23]

The production of a spermatophore by the male, in the cases
where the gelatinous matrix is prominent, represents a considerable loss of protein. In some crickets, for example, the loss may
amount to as much as 40 per cent. of the body weight.[15] In some
insects where the spermatophore protrudes from the genitalia
of the female after copulation, the female eats it. This phenomenon is common among the orthopteroid orders—in *Mantis* and
Oecanthus, for example.[99, 129] Whether or not the protein ingested
in this manner has any significance in the general nutrition of the
female is uncertain, but since egg development is often triggered
by copulation, the protein requirements of a recently mated female
are likely to be high. Nevertheless, devouring the spermatophore
may represent a distinct hazard to the successful completion of
the process of insemination and in *Oecanthus*, for example, the
female feeds on a secretion of the metathorax of the male during
the quarter-hour which is required for the transport of the semen
out of the spermatophore.[129] At the end of this time the female
eats the spermatophore. Many Lepidoptera and Neuroptera
secrete proteolytic enzymes into the bursa after copulation and
thereby digest the spermatophore. Whether the digested material
is absorbed or expelled is uncertain. Nothing is known of the
processes which control the secretion of the enzymes. In many
cases the spermatophore is simply expelled from the bursa after
varying periods in the female. The protein produced by the male
is thus lost, and this loss may constitute one of the factors leading
to the replacement of the spermatophore by more direct methods
of semen transfer.

At least part of the epithelium of the bursa in many insects is
secretory. Very little is known of these glandular cells. In
insects which digest the spermatophore, they may be responsible
for secreting the enzymes involved.[63] A number of other hypotheses have been put forward but none of these has been tested
adequately. There is some evidence that the cells are most

active in Lepidoptera when a spermatophore is present in the bursa.[124]

The transport of the semen from the spermatophore to the spermathecae in *Rhodnius* is a consequence of contractions in the oviducts. How far such a mechanism applies in other species is uncertain. Some of the accessory glands of the male of *Periplaneta* contain a pharmacologically active material[24] and rhythmic movements of the oviducts have been observed in recently mated Lepidoptera, Neuroptera, Trichoptera and Coleoptera. An

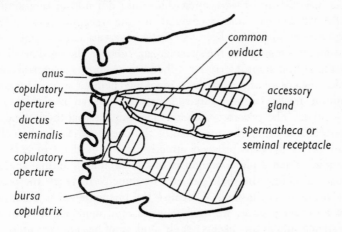

FIG. 13.   Diagram to show the female genital ducts in *Zygaena* (modified after Hewer).

opaque, milky secretion, similar in optical properties to the secretion in *Rhodnius*, is invariably associated with the spermatophore in these orders.[21]

The route which the spermatozoa follow is particularly complex in the Lepidoptera. Within the order there is a tendency towards more and more complete separation of the ducts involved in copulation from those involved in egg laying. In *Zygaena*, for instance, the opening to the bursa is completely separate from the opening of the oviducts. The spermatheca or receptaculum opens into the oviduct which is connected to the bursa by a duct, the ductus seminalis (fig. 13).

The spermatophore containing the spermatozoa is placed in

D

the bursa so that it is directed into or near the ductus seminalis. From here the spermatozoa are transported to the spermatheca, a process which occupies about five hours in *Bombyx*[90] and which occurs between 12 and 18 hours after copulation in *Zygaena*.[45]

The mechanisms which bring about the migration of the spermatozoa from the bursa along the ductus seminalis to the receptaculum or spermatheca have not been analyzed in detail for the Lepidoptera. WEIDNER[124] describes an experiment in which spermatozoa entered a capillary tube, one end of which was inserted into the receptaculum, and did not enter a similar tube which was not connected to the receptaculum. This experiment, and other less systematic observations have led many authors to suggest that the spermatozoa follow a chemical gradient. While at first sight it may be difficult to see how the spermatozoa reach the spermathecae without invoking chemotaxis, considerable caution needs to be exercised before such an explanation is accepted. The process of chemotaxis implies that the individual spermatozoa sense the presence of the chemical involved so that they are enabled to proceed directly up the gradient of concentration. Such a phenomenon is unknown among animal spermatozoa although the male gametes of some ferns reach the ovary by means of chemotaxis. Because the phenomenon is unknown among other groups, we must require rigid demonstration of its existence among the insects; such rigid proof has not yet emerged.

Nevertheless, it may be that the transport of semen in some insects, particularly the Lepidoptera, is an active process on the part of the spermatozoa. Thus in *Bombyx*, the spermatozoa are said to enter the spermathecae without being accompanied by the seminal fluid.[90] If the movements of the spermatozoa are necessary for the transport to occur (it is important to emphasize that there has been no experimental evidence to support this supposition), the phenomenon of rheotaxis may be involved. In this process, the spermatozoa become aligned against the direction of flow of the medium in which they are moving. In *Bombyx*, for instance, copulation triggers the activity of the spermathecal gland so that a copious flow of secretion from the receptaculum into the ductus results.[124] This flow may serve to orient the spermatozoa. Again, any material which affects the activity of the spermatozoa will influence the direction in which they move. In this way a high concentration of an activating material will repel the spermatozoa even though the movement of individual spermatozoa is random in direction.   Conversely any material which retards movement will result in an accumulation of cells in the area of highest concentration of the inhibitor.   Note that although the effect of these processes is the same as that of chemotaxis, the mechanism is quite different.   It is the level of activity of the spermatozoa and not the direction of movement which is influenced.   These processes belong to the class of behavioural reactions to stimuli known as kineses.   Whether kineses play any part in the transport of spermatozoa in insects is uncertain.   The male accessory glands of some Lepidoptera, Diptera and Coleoptera are said to contain activating substances.[86, 91, 129]   It may be that the presence of an activator in the seminal fluid assists in the movement of the spermatozoa out of the bursa, which in some species is not well equipped with muscles.

It is clear, however, that most or all of the transport of the semen within the females of Lepidoptera is associated with contraction of the various ducts.   In *Zygaena* for instance, pieces of debris from the disintegrating spermatophore are carried along with the spermatozoa by muscular contractions of the bursa and ductus seminalis.   These bits of debris are filtered out by the spinose intima of the upper ductus and contractions of the common oviduct and spermatheca are held to propel the spermatozoa into the receptaculum.[45]   Contractions of the ducts of the female are an almost invariable feature of recently mated females of those species in which the male does not deposit the semen directly into the spermatheca.

The transport of the semen from the spermatophore to the spermatheca of *Gryllus domesticus* is effected in an unusual way. The spermatophore (fig. 14) is a complex structure, which is produced by the male in advance of copulation.   The ampulla of the structure remains outside of the female genitalia while the long neck of the spermatophore penetrates into the female ducts. The semen is contained in a sperm sac, from which it is expelled by the expansion of two ' pressure bodies '.   These structures swell as they take up the evacuated fluid which moves across the various membranes separating it from the pressure bodies by osmosis.[62]   This phenomenon is probably not widespread among insects, as it has been described only for crickets. The spermatozoa are said to move from the tip of the spermatophore into the spermatheca by their own movements.

Another peculiar mode of insemination is to be found among the Cimicidae (Heteroptera) and their relatives. In the bed-bug, *Cimex lectularius*, the male deposits the semen by penetrating the cuticle over the organ of Berlese, which is situated on the fifth sternite of the female (fig. 15). The left paramere of the male is modified into a sharp stylus in order to effect the penetration.

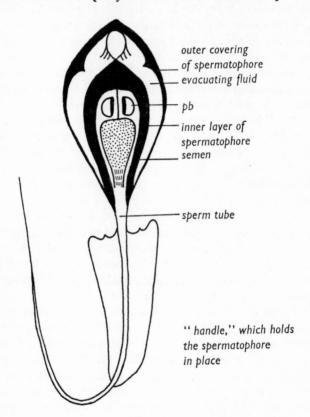

outer covering
of spermatophore
evacuating fluid

pb

inner layer of
spermatophore
semen

sperm tube

" handle," which holds
the spermatophore
in place

FIG. 14. Diagram of the spermatophore of *Gryllus domesticus*
(after Khalifa).

pb, pressure bodies, which take up evacuating fluid and
force semen out of the spermatophore.

The aedeagus fits into a groove in the paramere and carries the semen into the organ of Berlese. The spermatozoa find their way to the periphery of the organ of Berlese and in an area where there is a large concentration of spermatozoa, the wall between the organ of Berlese and the haemocoele breaks down, permitting the spermatozoa to enter the haemocoele. The spermatozoa next appear in the lumen of the ' sperm reservoir ' of the female. These organs are pouches, one leading off each of the lateral oviducts; while they function for a time as spermathecae, they are not homologous

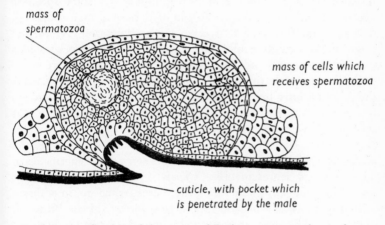

mass of
spermatozoa

mass of cells which
receives spermatozoa

cuticle, with pocket which
is penetrated by the male

FIG. 15. Section of the organ of Berlese, or spermalege, of *Cimex* (after Davis).

with the true spermathecae of other Heteroptera. Presumably the spermatozoa enter the sperm reservoirs by penetrating the wall from the haemocoele. The spermatozoa remain in the reservoirs until the female has her next blood meal, when they become oriented into packets and are transported up the oviducts to the ovaries where the developing eggs are fertilized before the shells are deposited. An unusual and interesting feature of this migration is that it is said to occur not in the lumen of the oviducts but in the tissues of the wall.[27]

The situation in *Cimex* is widely known and referred to as a ' typical ' example of haemocoelic insemination. It is increasingly apparent, however, that *Cimex* represents only one stage in a long evolutionary series. A recent publication[54] gathers together the observations on haemocoelic insemination in the cimicoid Heteroptera and proposes a sequence of events in which the first stage is represented by a Nabid, *Alleorhynchus plebejus*. In this species, after a normal insemination into the bursa, part of the migration of the spermatozoa to the ovaries (where fertilization occurs) takes place between the muscle fibres of the oviducts. Some of the spermatozoa accidentally penetrate into the haemocoel where they are phagocytosed. In the next step, represented by a number of Nabidae and Lyctocorinae, the spermatozoa are injected into the haemocoel through the wall of the bursa. In some species a special organ, the spermalege (organ of Berlese of many authors), develops and functions to receive the spermatozoa. A further stage in the evolution of haemocoelic insemination occurs in a Cimicid, *Primicimex cavernius*, in which the spermatozoa are introduced by the male through the outer integument of the female, the point of entry being different for each copulation. There are no spermalege. Eventually a particular area on the integument is specialized, with an associated spermalege, to receive the stylus of the male. The mesodermal portion of the spermalege, the mesospermalege, invariably phagocytoses some of the spermatozoa. This stage is represented by *Cimex*. A further development occurs in some species in which the mesospermalege, in addition to its functions as a phagocytotic organ, forms a tissue bridge to the ovary. The spermatozoa travel within this bridge rather than through the haemocoel. This stage is represented by a wide variety of Cimicids.

According to HINTON,[54] the adaptive value of haemocoelic insemination lies in the nutrition which the female receives from the phagocytosed spermatozoa and seminal fluid. Many of the Cimicoidea are parasitic; they are opportunists with respect to feeding in that they ingest very large meals when a host is available. On the other hand, the intervals between meals may be very great. The small amount of additional energy provided by phagocytosed spermatozoa might, it is argued, be sufficient to maintain the female for a short time until an opportunity for feeding presents itself. Perhaps the most convincing evidence in support of this idea comes from the males of *Afrocimex*, which possess spermalege similar to those of the females. Furthermore these spermalege are functional in that scars indicative of insemination from another male can be found in them. In this case the acceptor receives a small protein meal from the donor in the form of spermatozoa and seminal fluid. This small protein meal presumably increases the acceptor's resistance to starvation. At the same time the donor decreases its resistance, but if some males were to act as acceptors more frequently than donors, the survival value of such behaviour might be very great. An experimental investigation of this phenomenon would be very worthwhile.

The mode of transfer of the semen in the Odonata is entirely unique. The copulatory organs of the male are situated on the second and third abdominal sclerites, but the gonopore opens on the ninth segment, where there are rudimentary genitalia homologous to those in other groups. The functional intromittent organ, however, consists of a sclerotized tube on the third segment lying in a depression on the second. Before copulation occurs, the male bends the tip of the abdomen ventrally so as to transfer the semen to a reservoir on the intromittent organ. During copulation, the male uses the terminal cerci to grasp the female by the thorax, neck or head. The female then brings the end of her abdomen forward to the ventral surface of the male so as to join the female gonopore (on the end of the abdomen) to the intromittent organ of the male. This is accomplished while the insects are in flight.[55, 109]

The act of mating in insects frequently involves complex patterns of behaviour. The literature describing the various aspects of courtship in insects is voluminous and no attempt will be made to do it full justice. The account which follows is simply a selection of some of the phenomena which illustrate certain general aspects of reproductive behaviour.

Before the specific behaviour associated with copulation can be released, the sexes must of course come into comparatively close proximity. This can be accomplished in a variety of ways. Perhaps the best known mechanism for the attraction of the sexes is that of olfaction. In some insects, particularly among the Lepidoptera, the female secretes a volatile material, the perception of which by the male elicits locomotory activity which brings the male into the vicinity of the female. In some instances the mechanism has been known to operate over very long distances and at enormous dilutions: the male of *Bombyx mori* will respond to a glass rod moistened with a solution containing as little as 10^{-12} μgm./ml. of bombykol, the attractant which has been isolated from the females.[58]   Male attractants are known in a number of species from the Hymenoptera, Diptera and Coleoptera as well as the Lepidoptera.   In many cases the volatile material has been isolated and identified; the molecules responsible appear to have little in common chemically.[135]   Females emitting the odour often take up a characteristic ' calling ' posture in which the tip of the abdomen is raised and the glands responsible for the emission of the odour exposed.[87]   The males perceive the odour through chemoreceptors on the antennae and respond by taking flight.   The eventual location of the female by the male need not demand very complex patterns of behaviour, especially if the male responds, as has been suggested, by flying into the wind.

Another phenomenon which often precedes copulation and which is probably important in bringing the sexes together is that of aggregation.   The relationship between aggregation or swarming and mating has been extensively examined in the nematocerous Diptera.[31]   According to this study swarms of flying males develop above ' markers ', which are features of the landscape that occur rarely.   The development of the swarm is not a consequence of gregariousness but occurs as a result of the response of individual males to the marker.   As more and more males enter the area over the marker the swarm grows in size.   Even where two species swarm over the same marker, the swarms often occur at different heights so that separation of the two species is maintained. While males predominate in the swarm, females also respond to the marker and enter the swarm where mating takes place.   Once the sexes have been brought into relative proximity, the male is attracted to the female by auditory or visual means.   In some Nematocera swarming does not occur, but its equivalent is to be found in the attraction of both sexes to the same mammalian host upon which only the female feeds or in the relative immobility of some species which tend to remain near the sites of larval development.   Such mechanisms, that is, the attraction to feeding sites or oviposition sites, are possibly important in bringing together the sexes of other groups of insects as well.

Auditory stimuli play an important part in the meeting of the sexes in many insects. Certainly in mosquitoes the males are attracted to the females over short distances within the swarm by the sounds produced by the vibrations of the wings of the female.[100] Crickets produce a cycle of sounds associated with mating. In some species, the intensity of the chirping increases as the accessory glands responsible for the production of the spermatophore become distended with their secretions. After copulation, when the glands are partially empty, the intensity of the song decreases until more secretion is elaborated. Thus the intensity of the singing, and hence the likelihood of copulation, is related directly to the protein metabolism of the male.[15] In *Gryllus*, the song characteristic of courtship is produced only when a spermatophore is present in the female.[56]

Visual stimuli also serve to attract the sexes. In the beetle *Photinus pyralis*, the firefly or lightning bug, both the males and the females produce flashes of light from photogenic organs on the abdomen. The females respond to the flashing of the males by themselves flashing at a fixed time after the flash from the male. The male is by this means able to distinguish the females from other males.[14] In some species of *Drosophila* mating does not occur in the dark.[106]

The same stimuli which serve to bring the sexes together may release copulatory behaviour. Thus, male mosquitoes which have been attracted to a tuning fork emitting the appropriate frequency will copulate with isolated female genitalia.[100] Male moths will attempt to copulate with pieces of paper which have been moistened with extracts of the attractant gland of the female.[129]

On the other hand, a whole series of complex items of behaviour during courtship may be necessary to release the actual copulatory behaviour. The literature abounds with descriptions and analyses of these patterns. Frequently chemical, visual and tactile stimuli may all be involved in the mating process. In the cockroach *Blatella germanica*, for example, the initial step in courtship is contact between the antennae of the male and female. Mutual tapping of the antennae leads to the typical courting posture of the male with raised wings. This behaviour is probably released not only by the act of tapping but also by odours emanating from the female and movements executed by her. The courtship of the male also involves release of the secretion from the tergal gland. The female moves up to feed on this secretion and this act in turn releases the act of copulation.[101]

Feeding during courtship or copulation is a widespread phenomenon among insects. A number of species in the orthopteroid orders feed on tergal secretions much as described above for *Blatella*. Reference has already been made to this phenomenon in *Oecanthus*, where the function of this behaviour is held to be that of preventing the female from devouring the spermatophore. In cockroaches, however, the spermatophore is enclosed in the modified sternites of the abdomen of the female; it is more likely in this case that feeding behaviour represents a means for enticing the female into a suitable position. Feeding associated with copulation in various species of the Empids (Diptera) forms a hierarchical series of bizarre patterns of behaviour. In some species copulation occurs on the ground without associated feeding. In other species courtship occurs in the swarm and involves the presentation to the female of an item of prey captured by the male. The female feeds on this prey while copulation occurs on the ground. In still other species, this process is elaborated in that the prey is first enclosed in a cocoon of silk before being presented to the female. In some species of this group a small object from the environment rather than prey is enclosed in the cocoon. Finally, the cocoon presented to the female is empty.[106]

The nervous mechanisms which control reproductive behaviour are only beginning to be understood. It is clear that the release of copulatory activity in the male results from the suppression of inhibitory impulses from the head. In *Mantis religiosa*, courtship is a hazardous undertaking for the male. When a male sights a female, he approaches her with imperceptible movements. In some cases the approach is, from the point of view of the male, successful, and a normal copulation ensues. In many cases, however, the approach of the male is such that the female treats him as an item of prey. Since the male approaches head first, he is decapitated. Decapitation, whether by the female or in experimental situations, releases copulatory behaviour. Various experiments indicate that the inhibitory centre is located in the suboesophageal ganglion.[99] Destruction of different parts of the brain in *Gryllus* will produce different sorts of song along with the appropriate behaviour. Thus, destroying a particular part of the brain will produce the chirping and behaviour characteristic of courting. Under normal circumstances, the courting behaviour is only released when nerve fibres from the last abdominal ganglion signal to the brain that a spermatophore is present. These signals presumably lead to the suppression of the inhibitory impulses flowing from the brain to the chirping centre in the thorax.[56]

Such behavioural mechanisms are possibly important in imposing reproductive isolation on sympatric species. The earlier literature has emphasized the so-called ' lock and key hypothesis ' which holds that the geometry of insect pairing is so precisely characteristic for each species as to prevent interbreeding. While there is no doubt that such anatomical blocks to hybridization may apply in some cases, in many other instances the failure of the intricate behavioural mechanisms may be more important. Thus, in two sympatric species of the genus *Chorthippus*, differences in the song is the only factor which prevents hybridization.[94] This general problem has been extensively investigated for several species of *Drosophila*; these findings are summarized by SCHNEIRLA.[106]

Most insects are promiscuous; both males and females may copulate many times with different partners. In a few instances, too frequent mating may have deleterious effects. In the parasitic Hymenopteran *Macrocentrus ancylivorus*, sex determination is by haploid parthenogenesis; that is, unfertilized eggs give rise to males and fertilized eggs to females (see Chapter 6). If the sex ratio is such that a large number of males is allowed to inseminate a small number of females, the bursae of the females become distended with spermatophores. In such circumstances, none of the spermatophores is properly placed within the bursa and none of the spermatozoa arrives at the spermathecae. As a result no eggs are fertilized and more males appear in the population.[36]

In some cases the female will accept only one male. The screw worm, *Callitroga hominivorax*, a serious pest causing myiasis of man and domestic animals in Mexico and southern U.S.A., is such an insect. This characteristic has been utilized in a spectacularly successful attempt to eradicate the pest from parts of the United States. The programme involved the mass rearing of some millions of screw worms to the pupal stage when the pupae were irradiated. The resulting adults of both sexes were sterile. The release of very large numbers of sterile flies into the population resulted in a high proportion of sterile matings. In a limited trial on an island off the coast of Florida, the flies were eliminated within three months. During 1958 and 1959, 3750 millions of sterile flies were released on the mainland, and the southern U.S.A. east of the Mississippi is now free of the pest. While many factors, including the monogamous nature of the fly, undoubtedly contributed to the success of the venture, it is not necessary that the insect in question be monogamous, and similar studies aimed at the control of a number of pests are now under way.[67]

5 : Ovulation, Fertilization and Oviposition

In Chapter 2 we saw that the ovary produced the eggs, each enclosed in an envelope of follicular epithelium. The terminal oocyte of each ovariole, when mature, is at least partially surrounded by the follicle cells. The follicular tissue is particularly prominent at the posterior end of the terminal oocyte where it frequently forms a distinct mass of tissue, referred to as the follicular plug. Before the oocyte can be fertilized with spermatozoa stored in the spermathecae, the oocyte must move out of the ovary into the common oviduct. In doing so, it ruptures the follicular epithelium and pushes past the follicular plug. This process is known as ovulation.

The cellular debris left behind after the oocyte ruptures the follicle may form itself into a compact mass at the end of the ovariole. The mass may be very prominent for a time, but it gradually degenerates. In some termites, this mass is yellow in colour,[129] and it may be for this reason that the structure has been called a corpus luteum. This is an unfortunate term because it may imply that the structure has some special significance in the reproductive physiology of the animal. Unlike the corpus luteum of vertebrates, however, this mass of debris has never been shown to undergo further development or to have any particular function.

Often fertilization and oviposition follow rapidly after ovulation. For this reason and because there is no external event other than oviposition to signal its occurrence, the phenomenon of ovulation has proved very difficult indeed to study. In many insects the terminal oocytes of each ovariole may be ovulated and spend some time in the pedicel of the ovary or the oviducts before they are fertilized and oviposited. Such a situation must obtain in those insects which, like many of the Orthopteroid orders, lay their eggs in groups (see, for example HIGHNAM[48]). There is some evidence to suggest that the phenomenon of ovulation might be controlled by hormones but the precise mechanisms which propel the eggs out of the ovary have been studied in only a few cases.

In *Aedes*, the follicular sheath may degenerate before the oocyte leaves the ovary. The oocytes in this case are thought to move into the lateral oviducts as the combined result of contractions of the network of muscles over the ovary and the more powerful movements of the lateral oviducts. The control of these movements appears to be nervous, emanating from cephalic and thoracic centres, although the experiments did not eliminate the possibility of endocrine control.[20] Of course, the process of ovulation may be assisted by the growth of oocytes anterior to the terminal ones: the rupture of the follicle may thus be assisted by increasing pressure in the ovary. The details of the mechanism of ovulation in insects are almost entirely unknown, and this area should prove to be a fruitful one for future research.

Like ovulation, fertilization in insects is an internal phenomenon; consequently what little information is available is based on conclusions drawn from anatomical observations. In insects, fertilization involves two different sorts of problems. On the one hand there is the problem associated with the entry of spermatozoa into the egg through the micropyle; on the other hand there are the mechanisms which bring about the release of spermatozoa from the spermatheca. These two phenomena may be very closely related in some insects. In many species the egg is precisely oriented within the common oviduct so that the micropyle is directly opposite the opening to the spermatheca. In *Drosophila* there is, in addition to the pair of spermathecae, a third structure, the ventral receptacle. During copulation, all three organs become filled with semen, but it is the ventral receptacle which functions during fertilization. The egg of *Drosophila* has a single micropyle which becomes aligned with the opening of the ventral receptacle (fig. 16).[86] In other species the orientation may not be so precise.   In *Rhodnius* the micropylar groove which encircles the egg at the anterior end becomes closely applied to the openings of the paired spermathecae.   In *Periplaneta* a variable number (up to 100) of funnel-shaped micropyles are clustered on one surface of the cephalic pole of the egg.   Spermatozoa are ejected as this part of the egg passes near the spermatheca.[29]

The mechanisms which release the spermatozoa from the

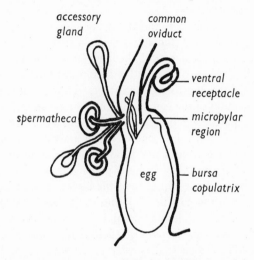

FIG. 16.   Diagram to show the fertilization of the
egg in *Drosophila* (after Nonidez).

spermatheca are largely a matter for conjecture.   In *Periplaneta* it has been suggested that the passage of the egg stimulates sensory hairs, thereby bringing about contractions of the muscles in the spermatheca.[29]   While something of this sort may very well occur in many insects, there is as yet no experimental evidence to suggest that the process is under nervous control.   Certainly there are anatomical arrangements in many insects which suggest that the spermatozoa are expressed by muscular contractions in the spermathecae.   Special muscles exist in a wide variety of forms. In other species in which obvious anatomical adaptations do not exist, it has been suggested that increased pressure in the haemocoel may drive the spermatozoa out of the spermatheca.[44]   In some

Hymenoptera the spermatozoa are held to be stored in the spermatheca in a quiescent condition. In such cases fertilization might involve the activation of the spermatozoa and their subsequent migration out of the spermathecae. The source of the activator in this case is supposed to be the spermathecal gland.[35] While this mechanism may apply in the case of the parasitic Hymenoptera which were studied, it is probably not of general importance as the spermatozoa of most other insects are active while they are in the spermatheca.

While for most insects the release of semen from the spermatheca is probably an automatic process which arises as a direct consequence of ovulation and the passage of the egg along the oviduct, it is clear that in some Hymenoptera the process is more directly under the control of the insect. In most of the Hymenoptera fertilization of the egg results in a female offspring, whereas unfertilized, parthenogenetically developing eggs are male. In honey bees the control is exercised in part by environmental factors since more drones are produced in the autumn than at other times of the year.[129] It has been suggested that an unfertilized egg is laid as a consequence of the larger cell in which drones develop. According to this hypothesis, the absence of pressure on the tip of the abdomen results in no spermatozoa being released when an egg is oviposited into a drone cell. On the other hand, the worker cell is very much smaller, and its walls would exert pressure on the abdomen resulting in a fertilized egg.[37]

The mechanism of fertilization in insects is remarkably efficient when compared to the situation in other groups of animals. In the parasitic dipteran, *Miastor*, for instance, the male produces only 512 spermatozoa per testis, or 1024 in all. The female lays 56 eggs. Assuming only one mating per female and that all of the spermatozoa from a single male are used to fertilize all of the eggs of a single female, we are presented with a figure of only 170 spermatozoa per egg.[125] Such precise estimates for other species are not available but in some of the social insects, where a single mating serves to fertilize all of the eggs produced by the queen, the efficiency may be even greater. Certainly the number of sperms released to fertilize a single egg must be several orders of magnitude less than is encountered among, for instance, the mammals, where the number of spermatozoa in a single ejaculate is of the order of 10^7.

The mechanism of entry into the egg of the spermatozoa has not been explored fully in the insects. In many cases the spermatozoa appear to be injected directly into the micropyle by the action of the spermatheca. In *Drosophila*, for instance, the egg pauses in its passage along the common oviduct so that the single micropyle is directly opposite the opening of the ventral receptacle.[86] Once in the micropyle, the spermatozoa presumably move along that structure to the vitelline membrane as a result of their own movements. In a large number of species, however, the spermatozoa are simply released from the spermatheca in the general region of the micropyle, and the spermatozoa must find their way into the micropyle. Often the micropyles are few in number and their course through the chorion may be tortuous. In *Rhodnius*, the micropyle is estimated to be as narrow as $0.5\ \mu$.[4] We have already seen that these characteristics of the egg are possibly adaptations to prevent loss of water, and that as a consequence there is a tendency for insects to produce filamentous spermatozoa capable of entering these narrow openings. These adaptations, however, impose serious difficulties associated with the entry of the spermatozoa into the egg. The diameter of the spermatozoa approaches that of the inner opening of the micropyle, and the length of the spermatozoa may exceed that of the micropyle. In these circumstances it is difficult to see how the spermatozoa penetrate into the micropyle without invoking some special mechanism.

Many authors have suggested chemotaxis as a possible mechanism for the entry of the spermatozoa into the micropyle. We have already dealt with this phenomenon in some detail in Chapter 4, and these remarks apply equally well in the present context. There has been no clear demonstration of a chemotactic response of insect spermatozoa to their eggs. In *Periplaneta*, at least, other mechanisms will explain the entry into the micropyle. The spermatozoa of *Periplaneta* tend to move in a curved path when they are swimming along a surface such as an egg. The spermatozoa are ejected from the spermatheca onto the surface of the egg near the micropyles, which are scattered over one surface of the egg. Since the outer opening of the micropyle in this species

E

is broadly funnel-shaped, some at least of the spermatozoa will eventually enter a micropyle.[29]   This phenomenon can be observed quite easily under a dissecting microscope using eggs from the ovary and spermatozoa from the seminal vesicles.

In *Rhodnius*, and probably some other species as well, the innermost layer of the chorion is a very thin wax layer, which extends over the micropyles both before and after fertilization.[3] It follows that the spermatozoa must penetrate this layer in order to accomplish the fertilization of the egg.   The mechanism of this penetration is completely unknown.   In various widely scattered species, the spermatozoa fertilize the eggs in the ovaries before the chorion is laid down.

Most of the other groups of animals possess mechanisms which ensure that only one spermatozoon enters the egg, but in insects polyspermy appears to be the rule rather than the exception. It is generally considered for other animals that the entry of more than one spermatozoon is likely to produce developmental difficulties.   This is also true in insects if the number of excess spermatozoa is very great but under normal circumstances only relatively few sperms enter the egg and the excess degenerate.[129] In some species the excess spermatozoa may actually enter into the development of the egg.   In the honey bee, for example, a fertilized egg normally gives rise to female (diploid) tissues. However, one or more of the excess spermatozoa involved in a polyspermic impregnation may enter into the development of the embryo independently and produce some male (haploid) tissues. The resulting gynandromorph is composed of some haploid and some diploid tissue.[102]   Under some environmental conditions, some species produce binucleate eggs, each nucleus of which is fertilized independently by separate spermatozoa.[129]

All of the structures which are embraced by the term ovipositor, as it is normally used by most entomologists, are not necessarily homologous.   The homologies of the various structures involved in egg laying are, however, quite clear.   In some insects the ovipositor is derived from abdominal appendages, in others it is simply composed of the modified terminal segments of the abdomen, while still other insects lack any definite ovipositor. In the Ephemerida, the two lateral oviducts open separately between the seventh and eighth sternites.   In all of the other orders, there is a common oviduct which opens on the eighth or ninth sternite. In those orders which possess an ovipositor composed of modified appendages, the opening tends to be on the eighth segment. While this type of ovipositor varies from group to group, the basic plan is usually quite apparent. The contention that this type of ovipositor is derived from segmental appendages rests on evidence from the Thysanura, where the ovipositor is obviously related to the abdominal appendages, and on observations on the development of the structure in various other insects.

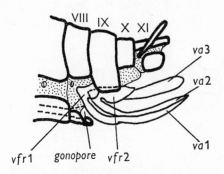

Fig. 17. Diagram to show ovipositor in a pterygote insect (after Snodgrass).

va1, *va2*, *va3*, first, second and third valvulae; *vfr1*, *vfr2*, first and second valvifers.

This evidence is presented in Snodgrass.[109] In insects possessing this sort of ovipositor, the eighth and ninth sternites each bear a pair of sclerites, the first and second valvifers. Each of the first valvifers, associated with segment eight, bears an additional, usually elongated, process, the first valvula. The second valvifers, on segment nine, each bear two such processes, the second and third valvulae. In most species it is the first and second valvulae which make up the prominent shaft of the ovipositor, while the third valvulae form a sheath for the distal end of this structure. Figure 17 is a diagram of the ovipositor in a hypothetical pterygote.

In many insects, especially those in which the gonopore is located on the ninth sternite, the ovipositor is absent or reduced. This is true in the Odonata, Plecoptera, Mallophaga, Anoplura, Coleoptera and the panorpoid orders. Some of the insects of this group, nevertheless, have an abdomen which is elongated and slender towards the tip and which functions as an ovipositor. It is important to realize, however, that such a structure has no homologies with the appendicular type of ovipositor described above. Orders in which the abdomen is modified to form an ovipositor include the Lepidoptera, Coleoptera and Diptera (fig. 18).

Since the larvae of most insects are not particularly motile, but are adapted rather for feeding, it follows that the selection of a suitable oviposition site by the female is a critical step in the life history. It is perhaps surprising, therefore, that we know so

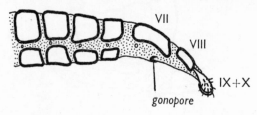

FIG. 18. Diagram to show how the terminal abdominal segments may be modified to assist in oviposition (after Snodgrass). Note that this is not a homologous ovipositor.

little about the phenomenon. Much of the selection of the general site for oviposition is, of course, a result of the attraction of the female to, for instance, host plants. A consideration of this phenomenon is obviously beyond the scope of this book, but the selection of suitable sites within the general area of oviposition appears to be at least partly a function of the ovipositor itself. The ovipositor of some species bears sensillae, chiefly chemo-receptors,[28] but the rôle which these sensillae play in the process of oviposition is not clear. It may be that stimulation of these receptors brings about ovipositional movements. Like copula-tion, oviposition seems to result from the suppression of impulses emanating from the head. Thus cockroaches which have been decapitated release their oothecae[101] and females of various species will oviposit immediately after decapitation.[19, 20] There is some evidence that the endocrine system may be involved in the control of oviposition (see Chapter 7). The mechanism which propels the eggs along the ovipositor, which in some insects may

be very long indeed, is unknown. This whole area of the phenomena surrounding oviposition should be a fertile one for future
investigation.

A few insects simply scatter their eggs indiscriminately in the
oviposition site. For instance the eggs of stick insects are dropped
by the females on to the forest floor. Other insects fasten the
eggs singly or in masses to the substratum. The adhesive which
fastens the eggs is a product of the accessory glands of the female.
In *Rhodnius* there is a single accessory gland opening into the
bursa and homologous with the spermatheca of other insects.
The secretion of this gland is a mucoprotein and is responsible for
fastening the eggs to their substratum.[25] Many of the Lepidoptera

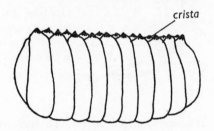

FIG. 19. Blattoid ootheca.

lay their eggs in masses which are cemented together by products
of the accessory glands. The eggs of the lace-wing, *Chrysopa*, are
supported on the end of a slender stalk composed of a silk-like
material. The process of oviposition may be extremely rapid in
some species. The females of the warble flies of the genus *Hypo-
derma* require less than a second to fasten an egg to the hairs on
the legs of cattle. The eggs of another warble fly, *Dermatobia*,
are normally laid on the body of another insect such as a mosquito,
which then carries the eggs to the mammalian host where the eggs
hatch.

Among the Orthopteroid insects many species have evolved
a further protective coating for the eggs, which are laid in pod-like
groups. Locusts, for example, lay their eggs in a pod which is
inserted in a hole in the ground dug by the abdomen and ovipositor. The hole is closed by a plug of frothy secretion. Mantids
lay their eggs in masses enclosed within a cocoon formed from the

secretions of the accessory glands. The oothecae of cockroaches have been intensively studied, especially those of *Periplaneta* and *Blatta*. These oothecae have the form of a purse and contain two parallel rows of eggs with the celphalic pole directed towards the ridge of the ootheca (fig. 19). The ootheca is extruded from the gonopore as the eggs are deposited in it, and is moulded in part at least by the action of the valvulae of the ovipositor. The oothecae may drop off after being carried for some time, or, in the case of the ovoviviparous cockroaches, the ootheca may be withdrawn into the ducts once more, where the eggs develop

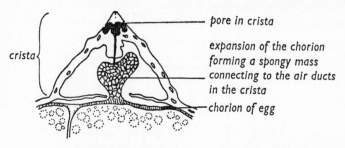

FIG. 20. Diagrammatic section through the crista of an ootheca to show respiratory modifications (after Wigglesworth and Beament). The path which the air takes is shaded in black.

inside the ootheca. In those cockroaches in which the ootheca is eventually deposited, the egg-case is composed of a material which resembles cuticle except for the fact that it contains no chitin. The colleterial glands, a pair of branching structures opening into the lower end of the oviduct are involved in the formation of the ootheca in *Periplaneta* and *Blatta*. The left colleterial gland secretes a protein and an oxidase. The oxidase acts on the protocatechuic acid secreted by the right colleterial gland to produce a quinone. The quinone in turn acts upon the protein to produce a tanning reaction. Calcium oxalate is also present in the ootheca; this has its origin in the left colleterial gland. Details of this process may be found in papers by PRYOR[95, 96] and BRUNET.[13]

Oothecae of this sort protect the eggs from desiccation, but at the same time present problems associated with respiration of the developing embryos. It is not, therefore, surprising to find that the oothecae are modified to permit gaseous exchange without undue loss of water. The ridge, or crista, of the ootheca is pierced on each side by a series of small holes. The chorion of the anterior pole of each egg is expanded and vacuolated. This expansion fits into a small cavity just beneath the crista and the cavity connects to the outside through the lateral openings on the crista (fig. 20).[129]

The production of an ootheca represents a considerable expenditure of protein which might otherwise have been used in the production of more eggs. This may be one of the factors contributing to their absence in higher orders. The accessory glands take over other functions in some insects. The stings of the Hymenoptera, for example, are modified ovipositors and the accessory glands are responsible for producing the venom involved.

6 : Unusual Methods of Reproduction

Thus far we have dealt with species in which the egg is fertilized internally, is oviposited and subsequently develops outside the mother. This represents the method of reproduction for the great majority of insects, but some groups have modified this basic scheme in various ways, leading to a diversity of unusual modes of reproduction, including parthenogenesis and other sorts of asexual reproduction, as well as viviparity. We shall deal with each of these phenomena in turn.

Parthenogenesis

In most insects the egg does not develop until after the fertilizing spermatozoon has brought about the process of activation. In several species, and occasionally in whole orders, the egg develops without the intervention of spermatozoa, that is, by parthenogenesis. In some species, chiefly among the stick insects and some aphids, males are unknown or very rare and parthenogenesis is obligatory and thelytokous (female-producing). In a large number of species, parthenogenesis is facultative and may be thelytokous, arrhenotokous (male-producing) or amphitokous (producing either sex). Thus, locusts normally reproduce bisexually but in the absence of males some females produce thelytokous eggs which develop by parthenogenesis.[42] Again, many aphids reproduce bisexually or parthenogenetically depending on the environmental conditions.

Sexual reproduction involves the fusion of two haploid nuclei, one from each parent, and thus offers the opportunity for the reassortment of genetic characters which in turn results in much of the phenotypic variation upon which natural selection acts. In parthenogenesis, which involves the development of an unfertilized egg, this opportunity for reassortment is absent. As a consequence, parthenogenetically reproducing populations should possess great genetic stability. At first sight at least, such genetic stability, by reducing the amount of variation upon which selection can act, appears to be a disadvantage as far as the continued survival of the species is concerned. At the very least there should be compensating advantages to be found in parthenogenesis. Where these advantages lie depends to some extent on which of the three types of parthenogenetic development is involved.

In apomictic parthenogenesis, there is no reduction in the number of chromosomes during oogenesis and the resulting diploid egg develops in the normal way. Typically only one maturation division occurs, and this is equational rather than reductional. In a few species, there may be two maturation divisions, both equational. Apomictic parthenogenesis occurs in the aphids, a few Orthoptera, the Tenthredinidae and some Chironomids and Cecidomyids.

Since meiosis does not occur, there is no opportunity for the crossing-over of chromosomes which is a feature of the normal meiotic process. Apart from mutations, then, the offspring retain the genetic constitution of the mother. A population which continues to reproduce by apomictic parthenogenesis will, therefore, become progressively more heterozygous. Thus the benefits which accrue from apomictic parthenogenesis are those of increased heterosis—a general increase in the efficiency of homeostatic mechanisms leading to an increased tolerance of varying environmental conditions.

Automictic parthenogenesis, on the other hand, involves the normal meiotic divisions which produce a haploid egg. The diploid number of chromosomes is restored by fusion of two nuclei. The nuclei involved are the egg nucleus and the second polar nucleus, or occasionally two cleavage nuclei. Automictic parthenogenesis occurs in the Phasmids, some of the Homoptera, notably the Aleurodidae, the Psychidae among the Lepidoptera and a few Diptera and Hymenoptera.

Since meiosis occurs in the production of automictically

developing eggs, there is opportunity for crossing-over. The genetic consequences of automictic development depend to a large extent on which nuclei fuse to form the zygote. Thus, if two cleavage nuclei fuse, the zygote will be homozygous and any heterozygotes which arise by mutation will be eliminated in the succeeding generation. If the egg nucleus fuses with the polar nucleus, the genetic consequences depend on whether the alleles in question separated at the first or second meiotic division. If they separated at the first meiotic division, the nucleus of the second polar body will resemble the egg nucleus and homozygosity will tend to replace heterozygosity. If the alleles in question separated at the second division (i.e. post-reductionally), heterozygosity, if present, will be maintained. Thus automictic parthenogenesis of this type may, if the parent is already heterozygous with respect to a number of genes, give rise to offspring which are either homozygous or heterozygous. Nevertheless, it is apparent that for automictic reproduction in general, homozygosity will gradually increase. In other words, there is a distinct tendency for any new mutation to become homozygous and an automictic species has the opportunity of initiating a number of distinct races.

More interesting, perhaps, is haploid parthenogenesis in which the oocytes undergo the regular meiotic divisions. The haploid egg thus produced may develop either by parthenogenesis in which case the offspring is male, or by fertilization in which case females are produced. Haploid parthenogenesis, then, is always arrhenotokous or male-producing. It is important to note that the males resulting from such arrhenotokous development are haploid in their somatic tissues as well as in their germ cells. The meiotic process which leads to the production of spermatozoa has been modified in various ways in order to accomplish this.[126] The phenomenon is widespread among the Hymenoptera and occurs also in some Homoptera, Thysanoptera and Coleoptera.

Since the production of females involves the normal reproductive process, it might be thought that the genetic consequences of haploid parthenogenesis are not very different from those of normal sexual development. Since the males are haploid, however, any recessive allele which arises by mutation will be expressed in the males and will therefore be subject to selection. Haploid parthenogenesis, then, offers great opportunities for favourable recessives to be established in a population. On the other hand, there is no opportunity for a concealed pool of recessive genes, which is so important in the evolution of forms reproducing normally. Moreover, the females in populations reproducing by haploid parthenogenesis will be more homozygous than in animals with diploid males.

The main advantages to be found in any form of parthenogenesis, of course, have little to do with genetics *per se*. A form reproducing parthenogenetically has a greater biotic potential because each individual produces eggs. Moreover, since fertilization is unnecessary, the parthenogenetic species do not have to rely on the meeting of sexes for reproduction, an advantage which must be particularly attractive to parasitic forms. Further details concerning the genetic aspects of parthenogenesis may be found in the recent reviews on the subject.[30, 61, 108, 113, 126]

Reproduction by parthenogenesis presents certain problems related to the determination of sex in the offspring. Even in forms reproducing sexually, the situation is by no means entirely clear for each species which has been investigated. In general, the determination of sex rests on the balance between several male-producing genes, several female-producing genes and, in many cases, environmental factors. The males of most insects are heterogametic and the *x*-chromosome carries the genes for femaleness. In these species the female has two *x*-chromosomes in each of her somatic cells and the male has one *x*- and one *y*-chromosome. In the Lepidoptera the situation is reversed: the *x*-chromosome carries the genes for maleness and the males are therefore homogametic. Individuals with two *x*-chromosomes are male, while those with one *x*-chromosome and one *y*-chromosome are female. In a few species there is no *y*-chromosome; in some cases the monosome occurs in the male but in the Lepidoptera it occurs in the female.

Much of the work on sex determination in general rests on observations on insects, particularly *Drosophila*. In this species it is held that the genetic determination of sex involves the balance between factors for femaleness on the *x*-chromosome and factors for maleness on the autosomes. This hypothesis is supported by studies on a number of mutants with differences in the ratio between the number of x-chromosomes and the number of autosomes (X/A). Where X/A is 1, the individuals are normal females; if the ratio is greater than 1, they are super-females, and may be sterile if the value is very high. Conversely, if the value of X/A is 0·5, normal males are produced, and at lower values super-males result. If the ratio lies between 0·5 and 1, the offspring are intersexes. In this case the y-chromosome is sexually blank.

In the Lepidoptera the results of similar breeding experiments indicate that once more the genetic determination of sex depends on a balance between male and female genes. Lepidopterous males are homogametic and the x-chromosome carries the genes for maleness. Under normal circumstances an individual with two x-chromosomes is male and one with an x-chromosome and a y-chromosome is female. In this case, however, it appears that the y-chromosome is not sexually blank and that it carries the genes for femaleness. This hypothesis rests on experiments with different races of the gypsy moth *Lymantria dispar* and the silkworm *Bombyx*. A detailed account of this evidence and that for the case represented by *Drosophila* may be found in textbooks of genetics and in a recent review.[61]

The environment may also affect the sex of the offspring. In some instances the effect is quite simple. Thus in *Talaeporia* (Lepidoptera) high temperatures tend to produce more males, while low temperatures produce more females than the expected 1:1 ratio. This is explained by the effect of temperature on the movements of the x-chromosome during oogenesis. High temperatures favour the appearance of the x-chromosome in the female pronucleus while lower temperatures cause it to appear in the polar body.[129] The environment may intervene at a different level of control. In the Isoptera and social Hymenoptera genetically determined females may be prevented from becoming functional reproductives by the action of various pheromones (see Chapter 7), or in the case of bees, by nutritional factors. The appearance of sexual forms in aphids is under the control of light and temperature.[70]

The foregoing explains the determination of sex in some of the forms reproducing sexually. How far can these principles be said to apply to forms which reproduce by parthenogenesis? In automictic, thelytokous parthenogenesis, the mechanisms seem fairly straightforward. Because some form of nuclear fusion occurs, the offspring should have the same genetic constitution as the mother and will of course be female. This will be true for the cases in which the female has two x-chromosomes. The Lepidoptera, however, have one x-chromosome and one y-chromosome in the female. In most cases, parthenogenesis is facultative and amphitokous; the parthenogenetic process gives rise to offspring of either sex. In those Lepidoptera in which parthenogenesis is obligatory and thelytokous, such as some of the Psychids, the fusion must presumably be between the female pronucleus and the polar body. If two cleavage nuclei fuse, the offspring would be either xx (i.e. male) or yy, which is presumably unviable. The production of females by parthenogenesis in aphids is readily explained, but the males are also produced by parthenogenesis. Sex determination in aphids is of the type in which the female has two x-chromosomes and the male has only one; there is no y-chromosome. In *Tetraneura*, eggs which are destined to produce males undergo a degenerate meiosis in which only the x-chromosomes form bivalent pairs. These fail to divide and one of the x-chromosomes is eliminated in the polar body.[70] This process must be under the control of the environment, since changes in the environment are known to influence the sex ratio.

The case of arrhenotokous or haploid parthenogenesis presents more difficulty and several hypotheses have appeared. One theory holds that the genes for femaleness in the chromosomes could not overcome the tendency for maleness resident in the cytoplasm of the egg in a haploid individual. On the other hand, a considerable part of the egg can be eliminated experimentally without affecting the sex of the individual. Another hypothesis postulates a multi-allelic gene governing sex. Females occur when the individual is heterozygous for the gene, males when the individual is hemizygous. Homozygous individuals will be male, but are held to be so effete that they die early in development. There is some evidence which supports this notion in some Hymenoptera but the high larval mortality which should occur under these circumstances is not an invariable feature of all of the species examined. A third, more complex, hypothesis involves a series of genes governing maleness and a second series governing femaleness. The effects of the genes for maleness are held to be the same whether they occur as homozygotes or hemizygotes. The effects of the female genes on the other hand are cumulative such that the tendency to femaleness would be greater in insects homozygous for these genes. In haploid parthenogenesis, females arise when the egg is fertilized, i.e. when the diploid number of chromosomes is present. Under these circumstances there will be a double tendency towards femaleness, and since a double set of male genes has the same value as a single set, the female tendency will predominate. In a male, or haploid, individual, there would be a single set of both male and female genes; in these circumstances the tendency towards maleness predominates. There is some experimental evidence to support this hyopthesis; this evidence along with details of the other hypotheses can be found in KERR.[61]

Viviparity

Most insects deposit their eggs shortly after fertilization and development continues outside the mother. A number of widely scattered species, however, give birth to more advanced stages. This phenomenon of viviparity takes a number of distinct forms. In ovoviviparous insects, the eggs are supplied with enough yolk during oogenesis to maintain the developing embryo. There is no direct connection between the developing embryo and the maternal tissues and the egg simply develops within the female reproductive organs. This type of viviparity is widespread; most of the viviparous cockroaches, for example, belong to this group.

An extension of ovoviviparity is to be found in some of the Diptera where the larva resulting from the ovoviviparous development of the egg is retained within the mother and nourished by her. This mode of reproduction is characteristic of the tsetse flies (Glossinidae) and has been designated as adenotrophic.[41] In *Glossina*, a single egg from one of the two ovaries enters the uterus after it is fertilized and within a day the first instar larva hatches. At this time the accessory glands, or so-called 'milk glands', enlarge and become active (fig. 21). The larva attaches itself by its mouth to the papilla-like opening of the glands into the uterus and is nourished by the secretions. In *Glossina* the larva remains in the female until it is mature; larviposition follows and the pupa is formed outside the mother. In the Hippoboscidae and related families, the larva continues to reside in the uterus until after pupation has occurred. It is a corollary

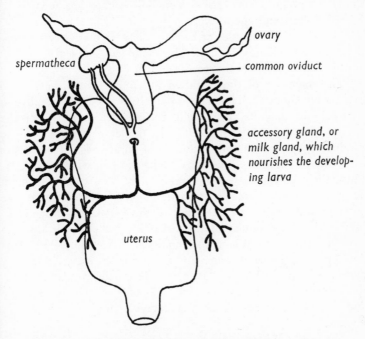

ovary

spermatheca

common oviduct

accessory gland, or milk gland, which nourishes the developing larva

uterus

FIG. 21.   Internal female reproductive organs of *Glossina* (after Hagan).

of this type of development that the ovaries be quiescent during the time that the larva is in the uterus. Such a phenomenon presumably involves the endocrine system. These presumed endocrine relationships await description.

A third type of viviparity involves the development of the embryo and larva in the haemocoel of the mother, and is designated as haemocoelous viviparity.[41] The egg receives its nourishment through its delicate serosa and the resulting larva feeds on the maternal tissues. This type of reproduction is normally associated with the phenomenon of paedogenesis, in which the ovaries of

larval insects undergo a precocious maturation. Not all paedo-
genetically reproducing insects develop their eggs in the haemocoel. Since aphids contain embryos in their ovaries when they are
born, they must be considered as paedogenetic. Paedogenesis
is normally associated with some form of parthenogenesis but in
the Heteropteran *Hesperoctenes*, a single specimen has been found
in which eggs and sperm were present in a last stage nymph.[40]
The best known examples of haemocoelous viviparity come from
among the Cecidomyidae and Chironomidae, but a few beetles
and the Strepsiptera also reproduce in this way.

The members of the Cecidomyid genus *Miastor* have been
extensively studied. The adult is oviparous and the larvae live in
a variety of habitats, principally rotting tree stumps. If the
environmental conditions are suitable, the larval ovaries begin to
produce oocytes, each with a number of nurse cells. The mature
ova burst out of the ovaries into the haemocoel, where they continue their parthenogenetic development. The ovaries contain
32 ova, but the more rapidly developing individuals at the
anterior and posterior extremities of the haemocoel are said to
inhibit the development of their sisters, so that fewer than 32
embryos survive. When the embryos have completed their
development, the larvae hatch and feed upon the maternal tissues,
particularly the fat body. The mature larvae ultimately penetrate
the maternal cuticle and emerge. Details of the embryology
and life history of these Cecidomyids may be found in
HAGAN.[41]

The beetle *Micromalthus* has an even more bizarre life history.
The paedogenetic larvae reproduce by one of two alternate
methods. One involves the production of a single large egg which
develops through a number of morphologically dissimilar larval
stages to become an adult male. Alternatively, a number of
larvae may be produced by haemocoelous viviparity. These also
pass through a number of morphologically dissimilar stages which
again have two alternatives for future development. The larvae
may either re-enter the paedogenetic cycle of reproduction or
they may pupate and produce a female. It would seem reasonable
to assume that the adults might mate and produce offspring in
the normal way. However, mating has never been observed and
the ovaries are in some respects degenerate. In view of this, some

authorities are inclined to the view that the adults, the male of which is haploid, are sterile.[41]

In the fourth type of viviparity, the developing embryo receives its nutriment through a pseudoplacenta. This type of development is to be found in some of the earwigs, the cockroach *Diploptera*, the aphids and various other species.

The nature of the so-called placental area varies from species to species. In the earwig *Hemimerus* the chorion is absent and the follicular cells at the anterior and posterior extremities of the mature oocyte multiply, possibly by amitosis, and form two spongy masses, referred to as the anterior and posterior maternal pseudoplacentae. These masses persist until well after the germ band has formed in the embryo when they begin a slow process of degeneration. At this stage, cells of the serosa and amnion opposite each of the maternal pseudoplacentae proliferate to form the larval elements of the pseudoplacenta. These also degenerate eventually but the anterior structure persists longer than the posterior. While the development and structure of these elements suggest a trophic function,[41] there is no evidence which suggests that materials from the mother continue to pass into the embryo after the yolk has been formed. In other species of earwigs these specialized structures are lacking; in aphids the chorion is also absent, and the follicle, which persists throughout development, is a very thin membrane.

In *Diploptera* the eggs retain the chorion, and the ootheca, which is characteristic of other cockroaches, is present in a reduced form. A feature of the development of the embryo is the hypertrophy of the pleuropodia, leg-like evaginations of the first abdominal segment. These are present as transitory structures in many other insects but in *Diploptera* they become very extensive and are eventually closely applied to the chorion. HAGAN[41] suggests that these outgrowths function in the nutrition of the developing embryo but again there is no real evidence to support such an assumption. *Diploptera* possesses a chorion through which the nutrients would have to diffuse. Furthermore the embryos are situated in the brood pouch of the female, the walls of which represent yet another barrier to the passage of nutrients from the haemocoel to the embryo. The eggs of most of the species which are designated as possessing pseudoplacentae

F

contain large quantities of yolk, and in *Diploptera* considerable quantities of the yolk remain in the gut at the time of hatching.[41] Until more decisive evidence is available it is as well to reserve judgement in this matter.

Polyembryony

In many parasitic Hymenoptera, and at least one species of Strepsiptera, the developing egg gives rise to more than one embryo. In both orders a trophamnion forms. In the Hymenoptera this is a derivative of the polar bodies; in the Strepsiptera it is derived from a cellular 'yolk', the ultimate origin of which is uncertain. The trophamnion serves to transport nutrients from the tissues of the host to those of the developing embryo. In the Strepsiptera, the tissues of the 'host' are those of the mother, since development is haemocoelous. In some Hymenoptera, division of the embryo occurs early; the products of the first cleavages may each form embryos. In the Strepsiptera, the polyembryonation occurs after a peripheral blastula-like mass of cells has formed. Division of this mass into several distinct groups occurs as the result of the centripetal invasion of the trophamnion. Many Hymenoptera undergo a similar sort of development. In any case the net result is the production of a large number of embryos from a single egg; in some cases the number of embryos so formed may be as high as 2000 in a single egg. This asexual phase in the life of some parasites is analogous to the parthenogenetic phase in aphids in that it affords the opportunity for the exploitation of a favourable environment when such is presented. In parasitic species this phenomenon is of paramount importance, because the environment suitable for larval development is discontinuous both in space and time. Details of polyembryony may be found in LEIBY[72] and in HAGAN.[41]

Alternation of Generations

Some insects are parthenogenetic only under certain environmental conditions and revert to sexual reproduction under other conditions. Perhaps the best known examples of this phenomenon occur among the aphids. While some species of aphids reproduce by parthenogenesis continuously, others exhibit an annual cycle in which parthenogenetic generations alternate with a sexual generation. Thus, in *Megoura viciae* the overwintering fertilized egg produces an apterous female which gives rise to daughters by parthenogenesis. This female is known as the fundatrix. A number of parthenogenetic generations, producing both winged and wingless females, ensues. In late summer the sexual forms, alate males and wingless females, appear. The proportion of males produced by a population can be suppressed by exposure to high or low temperatures. In some other aphids, the photoperiod to which the population is exposed also influences the production of males.[70]

The production of oviparous females is under the control of both temperature and photoperiod. Higher temperatures and longer day-lengths favour the appearance of viviparous parthenogenetic females, whereas lower temperatures and shorter day-lengths favour the appearance of the sexually reproducing, oviparous females. However, this picture is complicated by the operation of a timing mechanism whereby females separated by only a short interval of time from the fundatrix are less susceptible to the influence of temperature and photoperiod. Conversely the greater the time which separates the females from the fundatrix, the more susceptible are these females to the effects of light and temperature, i.e. the more likely they are to produce sexual forms. An interesting feature of this system is that the timing mechanism is one which measures time rather than the number of generations for the appearance of the sexual forms is a function of time and is independent of the number of generations. Furthermore, since the males tend to appear earlier than the females, there may in fact be two such timers.[69, 70]

We have already mentioned the alternation of generations which occurs in the Cecidomyid fly *Miastor* in which the asexual generations develop in the haemocoel of the mother. In the related *Oligarces paradoxus*, larvae developing from an egg give rise to further larvae by haemocoelous viviparity. This process may be repeated by the daughter larvae and may continue indefinitely. On the other hand, the larvae may give rise to pupae from which the sexually reproducing adults will emerge. The pupating larvae can be induced to appear by a variety of environmental conditions. For example, overcrowding the paedogenetic generation leads to the appearance of pupating larvae; changes in the diet will also induce the production of adults. The differentiation towards the adult form is at least partially reversible.[41, 129]

Those insects with an alternation between sexual and asexual forms possess a formidable potential for the exploitation of a favourable environment. The retention of the sexual, oviparous phase not only represents a means for getting the population through the severe environmental conditions of winter, but it also offers the genetic advantages inherent in sexual reproduction. On the other hand, the rapidly multiplying asexual phase exploits the favourable environment very quickly—witness, for example, the explosive increase in aphid populations in favourable summers. Furthermore the parthenogenetic phase spreads any favourable combinations of genes throughout the population more rapidly and in greater numbers than would perhaps be possible by sexual means.

7: Hormones and Reproduction

It is by now well established that the corpora allata of many adult insects secrete a hormone which controls the deposition of the yolk in the developing eggs. It is not proposed to review all of the evidence which bears on this statement. It is sufficient to say here that in a number of species extirpation of the corpora allata prevents maturation of the eggs and that changes in the cells of the corpora allata are correlated with the deposition of the yolk. The corpus allatum also controls metamorphosis: extirpation of the larval gland brings about premature expression of adult characters in the next instar. Whether one or two hormones are involved is uncertain. The weight of the evidence at the moment favours the notion that only a single hormone is involved. Extracts of the abdomens of male cecropia moths possess both juvenilizing and gonadotropic activity.[133, 134] Farnesol and its derivatives mimic the action of both the juvenile hormone and the gonadotropic hormone.[130] Certainly the corpus allatum of various adult insects appears to possess a titre of juvenile hormone sufficient to maintain juvenile characters when implanted into larvae. Conversely, larval corpora allata in *Drosophila* possess gonadotropic activity.[128] This evidence, while suggestive, is not at all conclusive. For instance, great caution should be exercised in interpreting the results of experiments involving substances with endocrine activity. Thus far there has been no evidence which demonstrates conclusively that any of the active materials tested appears in the corpora allata. It is possible that the two hormones are different but closely related compounds secreted perhaps by different cells in the corpus allatum and that the various active compounds are related to both of these hormones.

There are some insects in which other endocrine organs have been shown to play a rôle in the control of vitellogenesis. In *Calliphora*, for instance, neurosecretory cells from the pars intercerebralis of the brain have been implicated in the process. In this case, extirpation of the corpora allata, the neurosecretory cells or the corpora cardiaca (the storage organ from which the neurosecretory products are released) all will inhibit the growth of the ovaries. Removal of the corpora allata alone is not so effective as removal of the neurosecretory cells or the corpora cardiaca.[120] Histological differences in the neurosecretory cells have been correlated with the development of the ovaries and the size of the corpus allatum in *Iphita limbata*, in phasmids, and in *Schistocerca*.[48, 98] On the other hand, there are insects in which the neurosecretory cells of the brain appear not to be involved. In *Oncopeltus fasciatus*, eggs develop fully in the absence of the neurosecretory cells and in the ovoviviparous cockroaches, *Leucophaea maderae* and *Diploptera punctata*, the corpus allatum is under the control of nervous impulses from the brain and suboesophageal ganglion.[33, 57, 98] These results have led to the suggestion that the activity of the corpus allatum is under the control of the brain, and that this control may be either nervous or humoral.[48]

Mating often provides the stimulus which releases the hormones governing vitellogenesis. In *Schistocerca*, females which have been maintained in the absence of males produce eggs only very slowly and possess large amounts of neurosecretory material in the brain and corpora cardiaca. Similar females which have copulated, on the other hand, release their neurosecretory material and the oocytes mature very rapidly.[47, 48] The mere presence of the males, without copulation, also increases the rate of maturation of the eggs; this phenomenon is also mediated by the neurosecretory system.[49] The presence of males, as distinct from copulation, results in increased locomotor activity among the females. This phenomenon occurs in response to an odiferous secretion released by the males.[73] Since enforced activity in itself leads to release of neurosecretory materials and maturation of the eggs, it may be that the chain of events is: release of pheromone by male→increased locomotor activity in female →release of neurosecretory material→activation of corpora allata→maturation of eggs. There is, however, no specific evidence which connects all of these events causally. At any rate, under conditions in the field, mating would also trigger the release of the neurosecretory materials

In *Diploptera* and *Leucophaea*, relatively short periods of ovarian activity alternate with longer periods of quiescence. The cycles are under the control of the corpus allatum but the control of the corpus allatum is in this case nervous rather than humoral. Section of the nervi corporis allati, which runs from the brain to the corpora allata, activates the corpora allata and hence the ovaries of a quiescent female. During the quiescent periods the corpus allatum is apparently under the influence of inhibitory stimuli travelling in the nervi corporis allati. A virgin female remains under the influence of these inhibitory factors until mating intervenes. During copulation, sensory stimuli received in the terminalia travel in the abdominal nerve cord from the last abdominal ganglion to the brain, which then ceases to inhibit the corpus allatum. The glands become active, as evidenced by an increase in size, and the process of vitellogenesis is accelerated.[33, 34] Other species have not been examined in such detail but it is clear that mating often initiates or accelerates egg maturation. By analogy with other species it is probably safe to assume that the corpus allatum is involved in the control of this phenomenon. In the Oriental migratory locust, for instance, copulation, even by males which have been castrated, accelerates egg production. In this case, however, the stimulus does not arise from the terminalia, nor does it proceed via the nerve cord; according to the author, the stimulus is perceived over the general body surface during the sexual embrace.[97]

While it is obvious that nutrition will affect the maturation of the eggs in the sense that no yolk can be deposited without the necessary nutritional precursors, nutritional factors may also control the ovaries through the endocrine system. For instance, the eggs of starved *Leucophaea* do not develop. Implantation of active corpora allata, however, will bring about ovarian development in these starved females.[57] In this insect, then, starvation does not exert its effect directly on the oocytes but is mediated by the corpus allatum. This phenomenon has been studied in more detail in the blowfly *Calliphora erythrocephala*. If female blowflies are fed on diets rich in both protein and carbohydrates, their corpora allata increase in size up to the time of yolk deposition, when they decrease in size. If they are fed on carbohydrate alone, this cycle of events does not occur and the allata remain small. The increase in volume of the corpora allata is proportional to the amount of protein consumed and withdrawal of the protein from the diet results in a decrease in size of the corpora allata. Furthermore, the decrease in volume of the corpora allata which occurs at the time of yolk deposition can be prevented by feeding the flies large quantities of protein. The response of the corpus allatum to these fluctuations in protein in the diet are held to be a consequence of fluctuations in the content of protein metabolites in the haemolymph. The corpus allatum is thought to respond directly to the concentration of these metabolites rather than in any indirect way, as through the nervous system. In this way the increase in size of the corpus allatum before yolk deposition is due to the increase in titre of these metabolites. During vitellogenesis the metabolities are used in the production of yolk, the titre in the blood falls and the corpus allatum decreases in volume.[111, 112]

The median neurosecretory cells are also implicated in this cycle. We have already seen that the median neurosecretory cells are a *sine qua non* for vitellogenesis in the blowfly.[120] The median neurosecretory cells are also essential for the production of protease in the gut.[121] When flies without their median neurosecretory cells are offered the choice between diets rich in protein and those containing only carbohydrate, they choose the latter. Even when such flies are forced to ingest meals rich in protein, the meal is not digested because of the lack of protease.[112] Although the results are far from conclusive, they suggest that the effect of the median neurosecretory cells on the corpus allatum might be indirect. The hormone from the brain might act by enabling the fly to digest protein, which provides the necessary metabolites in the blood, thereby stimulating the corpus allatum. The results do not preclude the possibility that the effect of the hormone from the brain is a direct one; in this case the hormone would stimulate protein digestion and the activity of the corpus allatum. It is not even certain that the neurosecretory cells secrete a single hormone. The way in which the median neurosecretory cells influence the feeding behaviour of the flies is uncertain.

Similar observations have been made on the desert locust. In this species the total protein in the blood increases during yolk deposition, a period when the neurosecretory cells are also active. Removal of the neurosecretory cells results in a low titre of protein in the blood, and conversely treatments designed to release the neurosecretory material bring about a high concentration of protein in the blood. Since the free amino acids of the blood decrease when the protein is high and increase when it is low, it is suggested that the blood acts as a pool of amino acids for protein synthesis during yolk deposition. At least one of the proteins in the blood has been shown to be incorporated into the yolk. Evidently the synthesis of at least some of the proteins involved in vitellogenesis is under the control of the neurosecretory cells of the brain. Whether this is an effect on digestion as in *Calliphora*, a direct effect of the hormone or hormones involved on protein metabolism, or an indirect effect mediated by the corpus allatum is as yet uncertain.[50]

Probably not all of the species in which there is a dependence on nutritional factors for vitellogenesis possess such an elegant system of controls as *Calliphora* or *Schistocerca*. In *Aedes aegypti*, for instance, a blood meal is essential for the maturation of the eggs. Decapitation of fed females does not prevent the initiation of ovarian development, but does prevent the complete maturation of the eggs. Evidently the blood meal provides nutrient for the developing eggs as well as a stimulus releasing from the head a hormone which permits the utilization of these nutrients.[38]

During the periods when the ovaries of insects are said to be quiescent, there is in fact normally considerable cellular activity. The early stages of oogenesis proceed, usually up to the point where yolk would normally be deposited. In the absence of the corpora allata, however, the developing oocytes are resorbed, and the various nutrient materials from the developing egg are presumably returned to the fat-body or blood. In this way the reproductive potential of an individual is maintained. Whether or not these early stages of oogenesis are under the control of hormones is uncertain. In some species, the eggs are not resorbed.

In *Schistocerca*, for instance, we have already seen that females maintained in the absence of males have inactive corpora allata and mature their eggs only very slowly. The important point in the present context is that the eggs do mature, and in fact go on to develop parthenogenetically, thereby maintaining the reproductive potential. This development is presumably under endocrine control and the corpus allatum may be at least slightly active in a virgin female. The effect of mating must be to accelerate an existing process rather than to alter the endocrine balance in any qualitative way.

The mode of action of the gonadotropic hormone is still a matter for speculation. From what has already been said it is clear that during vitellogenesis, the protein metabolism of the female increases markedly, and many authors consider that it is this process which is controlled by the gonadotropic hormone. On the other hand, it is also clear that in some species the neurosecretory cells of the brain are also involved. On the evidence at present available, it is difficult to separate the effects of the corpus allatum from those of the neurosecretory cells. Nevertheless, there is a considerable body of evidence which suggests that the effect of the hormone might be on protein metabolism. There is a wealth of observations which show that during vitellogenesis protein reserves are mobilized from the fat-body into the blood and thence to the ovary. Furthermore, this mobilization is prevented in the absence of the corpus allatum. Thus, in the grasshopper *Melanoplus* the fat-body loses its reserves during vitellogenesis. In the absence of the corpus allatum the fat-body becomes greatly hypertrophied. Similar observations have been made on a number of species.[128] The fact that the fat-body hypertrophies is perhaps revealing. It is possible that the corpus allatum even at periods of relatively low activity secretes a small amount of hormone into the blood, thereby maintaining a low level of protein metabolism. If the corpus allatum were completely inactive at the time of low protein metabolism, then its removal would not be expected to lead to hypertrophy of the fat-body.

The discussion this far has dealt with factors which initiate or accelerate the secretion of the corpus allatum and vitellogenesis. In many short-lived insects, of course, all of the eggs of a particular

female are produced in single batch. In other insects the eggs
are produced in a series of batches, with periods of ovarian activity
alternating with periods of inactivity. Cockroaches, for instance,
carry their oothecae about for various, often considerable, lengths
of time. Since the ootheca blocks the genital ducts, it is obviously
important that the ovaries remain quiescent during this period.
In the ovoviviparous cockroaches such as *Leucophaea* and *Diploptera*, the period during which the ootheca is retained is greatly
prolonged. We have already seen that the corpus allatum in
these insects is normally under the influence of inhibitory impulses travelling in the *nervi corporis allati*, and that this inhibition
can be abolished by copulation. The production of an ootheca,
and its retention in the genital ducts, re-imposes the inhibition
on the allata and leads to a period of renewed quiescence in the
ovaries. In *Leucophaea* severing the abdominal nerve cord in
a virgin (in which the corpora allata are inactive because of the
absence of the mating stimulus) or in a pregnant female (in which
the corpora allata are inactive by virtue of the presence of an
ootheca in the brood sac) results in activation of the corpora
allata and deposition of yolk. The latter case has been examined
in more detail. Removal of the ootheca from the brood pouch
also results in activation of the corpora allata. The conclusion
at first sight appears to be obvious—that the presence of the
ootheca in the brood pouch sets up and maintains inhibitory
impulses in the nerve cord—but there may be other phenomena
involved. A closer examination of the results revealed that
maturation of the eggs required a significantly longer time after
severing the nerve cord than after removal of the ootheca. This
suggested that the egg case in the brood sac might release into the
blood factors which inhibit the corpus allatum. The observation
that injection of extracts of oothecae delays the maturation of the
eggs supports such a hypothesis. On the other hand, if such
factors are functional in the normal insect, then they may be
unspecific, since homogenates of muscle have the same effect.[33, 34]
We have already mentioned that the corpus allatum in some
species may be inhibited by the presence in the blood of high
concentrations of protein metabolites. Perhaps this phenomenon
may have some relevance to these experiments, which, after all,
involve the injection of materials rich in protein.

The control of development of the ovaries in social insects is of interest. The initiation of egg maturation by a pheromone in locusts has already been discussed. In the social insects a pheromone has the opposite effect. In general, a pheromone is secreted by an actively reproducing female in the colony and this pheromone inhibits the ovaries of other females. Presumably the inhibition is mediated by the endocrine system but direct evidence of such an effect is not available. In honey bees, for instance, the presence of an ovipositing queen in the colony inhibits the production of queen cells, and, more important in the present context, prevents the maturation of the ovaries of the workers. The material responsible for the production of these effects is a pheromone known as ' queen substance ' and identified as 9-oxdec-2-enoic acid. Queen substance is produced in the mandibular glands of the queen and is transmitted throughout the colony by the workers which lick it from the surface of the queen and distribute it to other workers in the food.[16, 17] The action of queen substance is not species-specific, since injections of the synthetic material into houseflies inhibits the ovaries.[84] Whether or not the action of queen substance is mediated by the endocrine system is uncertain, but the fact that the ovaries of worker bees continue to develop up to the stage where yolk is normally deposited suggests that the gonadotropic hormone is not active.

A similar, but more complex arrangement is to be found in the termites, where LUSCHER has analyzed the control in *Kalotermes flavicollis*.[74] In this species the full grown larva or pseudergate has four possibilities for further development at the next moult. One of these alternatives is for the pseudergate to moult to a sexually mature individual known as an accessory reproductive. As long as a pair of active reproductives is in the colony, no supplementaries of either sex are produced. The inhibitory stimulus involved is present in the faeces of the queen, and inhibition by the queen is only effective if a king is also present. A female alone is not so effective and will only inhibit the production of females. A king alone has no effect at all, although the presence of two males without a female will partially inhibit the production of male supplementaries. This suggests that more than one pheromone may be involved, a suggestion which receives

some support from a consideration of the way in which the pheromones are transmitted throughout the colony. This distribution
is extremely rapid, occurring in less than 24 hours. Since it would
be impossible for each individual in a large colony to contact the
queen once in 24 hours, the pseudergates themselves must be
able to transmit the stimulus to one another. LUSCHER'S experiments suggest that this is indeed so, but that the female pseudergates transmit only the male-inhibiting substance and vice-versa.
As a further complication, there is evidence which suggests that
an actively reproducing male secretes a substance which stimulates
the production of female supplementaries.

These effects are mediated by the endocrine system. The
moult itself, is, of course, under the control of ecdysone secreted
by the prothoracic glands. In addition, however, the corpora
allata increase in size just prior to the ecdysis to a supplementary
reproductive. This increase in activity of the corpora allata,
presumably under the control of the pheromones, is held to be
responsible for egg maturation in the female.

The corpus allatum, in some species at least, appears to be
involved in the control of reproductive behaviour. In *Leucophaea*,
as in many cockroaches, the mating behaviour consists of an
exchange of stimuli between the sexes in which an odorous
substance from the male serves to attract the female. Females
deprived of their corpora allata respond much less frequently
to the courtship of the males, and it is tentatively concluded that
the presence in the female of an active corpus allatum lowers the
threshold of the female for the perception of the male odour.[33, 34]
In *Bysotria fumigata*, another cockroach, it is the females which
secrete a pheromone to attract the males. In allatectomized
females, this attractant is not produced and the pattern of mating
behaviour breaks down. Implanting allata into allatectomized
females restores their ability to produce and secrete the
pheromone.[1]

The effects of the corpus allatum on the male are not so
spectacular nor so well documented. Male *Rhodnius* which have
been deprived of their corpora allata fail to elaborate the proteinaceous secretion which is responsible for the formation of the
spermatophore. This observation is an additional piece of
evidence supporting the hypothesis that the primary effect of the

corpus allatum is in stimulating the synthesis of protein. Since the distension of the accessory glands in other species is a factor in the control of behaviour, it is possible that some indirect control of reproductive behaviour may be achieved by the corpus allatum. Removal of the corpus allatum has no obvious effect on the production of semen.[127] It is important to remember, however, that in most insects the semen is produced in the stage preceding the adult. In this case, extirpation of adult corpora allata might not be expected to influence the production of the semen.

The process of spermiogenesis which produces only the cellular elements of the semen, is under the control of the prothoracic glands. In the large silk moth, *Platysamia cecropia*, the elongation of the spermatids is one of the first morphological events which signals the end of the pupal diapause. In the absence of the prothoracic glands, or of the neurosecretory cells from the brain which control them, diapause is not terminated and spermiogenesis does not take place.[105]

It is generally agreed that insects do not produce gonadal hormones. Thus, extirpation of either ovaries or testes is widely believed not to influence sexual development or behaviour. On the other hand, there are a number of reports in the literature concerning the effects of ovariectomy. In *Calliphora*, for instance, ovariectomy leads to hypertrophy of the corpus allatum and the selection of a diet rich in carbohydrate and low in protein. While these observations might be interpreted as indicating the presence of an ovarian hormone, a more likely explanation is that the removal of the ovaries brings about a rise in titre of the protein metabolities normally used in vitellogenesis. The high titre of the metabolites in the blood then influences the endocrine system.[112] Similar observations have been made on ovariectomized females of the bug *Iphita*,[83] and this evidence has been used to support the claim that there is a feed-back system involving an ovarian hormone and the rest of the endocrine system. However, the results from *Iphita* do not eliminate the possibility that the observed effects are brought about in the same way as in *Calliphora*.

The related phenomena of ovulation and oviposition may be under endocrine control in some insects. In *Iphita*, the presence of mature eggs in the ovary not only results in a decrease in the supply of the neurosecretory material which governs the activity of the corpora allata, but also is held to bring about the release of different neurosecretory materials which lead to ovulation and oviposition.[83] In *Schistocerca* the terminal oocytes of each ovariole mature synchronously and move out into the oviducts, where they may remain for up to a week. During this time there is a considerable synthesis of neurosecretory substance in the brain, but very little release of these products. During oviposition, this material is rapidly released into the blood and the next batch of oocytes begins to develop. Blood taken from an ovipositing female will induce movements typical of oviposition in other females. Various treatments designed to release the stored neurosecretory products will also initiate oviposition. Injection of extracts of corpora cardiaca, the storage organ for the neurosecretory products, initiates movements characteristic of oviposition. The blood of ovipositing females contains a pharmacologically active agent.[47] These observations constitute strong evidence for some sort of endocrine control of oviposition but the details of the functioning of such a system have yet to be worked out.

References

1. BARTH, ROBERT H., JR. 1961. Hormonal control of sex attractant production in the Cuban cockroach. *Science* **133**: 1598f.

2. BEAMENT, J. W. L. 1946. The formation and structure of the chorion of the egg in a Hemipteran, *Rhodnius prolixus*. *Quart. J. Micr. Sci.* **87**: 393–408.

3. —— 1946. The waterproofing process in eggs of *Rhodnius prolixus* Stahl. *Proc. Roy. Soc. B.* **133**: 407–18.

4. —— 1947. The formation and structure of the micropylar complex in the egg-shell of *Rhodnius prolixus* Stahl. (Heteroptera: Reduviidae.) *J. Exp. Biol.* **23**: 213–33.

5. BISHOP, G. H. 1920. Fertilization in the honey-bee. I. The male sexual organs: their histological structure and physiological function. *J. Exp. Zool.* **31**: 225–58.

6. —— 1920. Fertilization in the honey-bee. II. Disposal of the sexual fluids in the organs of the female. *J. Exp. Zool.* **31**: 267–83.

7. BLUM, M. S., GLOWSKA, S. and TABER, S. 1962. Chemistry of the drone honey bee reproductive system. II. Carbohydrates in the reproductive organs and semen. *Ann. Ent. Soc. Amer.* **55**: 135–9.

8. BONHAG, P. F. 1955. Histochemical studies of the ovarian nurse tissue and oocytes of the milkweed bug, *Oncopeltus fasciatus* (Dallas). *J. Morph.* **96**: 381–411.

9. —— 1955. Histochemical studies of the ovarian tissues and oocytes of the milkweed bug, *Oncopeltus fasciatus* (Dallas). II. Sudanophilia, phospholipids and cholesterol.

10. —— 1956. The origin and distribution of periodic acid-Schiff-positive substances in the oocyte of the earwig, *Anisolabis maritima*. *J. Morph.* **99**: 433–64.

11. —— 1958. Ovarian structure and vitellogenesis in insects. *Ann. Rev. Ent.* **3**: 137–60.

12. BONHAG, P. F. and WICK, J. R. 1953. The functional anatomy of the male and female reproductive systems of the milkweed bug, *Oncopeltus fasciatus* (Dallas) (Heteroptera: Lygaeidae). *J. Morph.* **93**: 177–284.

13. BRUNET, P. C. J. 1952. The formation of the ootheca by *Periplaneta americana*. II. The structure and function of the left colleterial gland. *Quart. J. Micr. Sci.* **93**: 47–69.

14. BUCK, J. B. 1938. Synchronous rhythmic flashing of fireflies. *Quart. Rev. Biol.* **13**: 301–14.

15. BUSNEL, R. G. and DUMORTIER, B. 1955. Etude du cycle génital du mâle d'*Ephippiger* et son rapport avec le comportement acoustique. *Bull. Soc. Zool. Paris*, **80**: 23–4.

16. BUTLER, C. G. 1959. The source of the substance produced by the queen honey-bee (*Apis mellifera* L.) which inhibits the development of the ovaries of the workers of her colony. *Proc. Roy. Ent. Soc. London A* **34**: 137–8.

17. CALLOW, R. K. and JOHNSON, N. C. 1960. The chemical constitution and synthesis of queen substance of honey bees (*Apis mellifera*). *Bee World* **41**: 152–3.

18. CARSON, H. L. 1945. A comparative study of the apical cell of the insect testis. *J. Morph.* **77**: 141–61.

19. CHIANG, H. C. and KIM, Y. H. 1962. Decapitation-initiated oviposition in Crane flies. *Ent. Exp. Appl.* **5**: 289–90.

20. CURTIN, T. J. and JONES, J. C. 1961. The mechanism of ovulation and oviposition in *Aëdes aegypti*. *Ann. Ent. Soc. Amer.* **54**: 298–313.

21. DAVEY, K. G. 1958. The migration of spermatozoa in the female of *Rhodnius prolixus* Stahl. *J. Exp. Biol.* **35**: 694–701.

22. —— 1959. Spermatophore production in *Rhodnius prolixus*. *Quart. J. Micr. Sci.* **100**: 221–30.

23. —— 1960. The evolution of spermatophores in insects. *Proc. Roy. Ent. Soc. London A* **35**: 107–13.

24. —— 1960. A pharmacologically active agent in the reproductive system of insects. *Can. J. Zool.* **38**: 39–45.

25. —— Unpublished data.

26. DAVIES, L. 1947. Laboratory studies on the egg of the blowfly *Lucilia sericata* (Meig). *J. Exp. Biol.* **25**: 71–85.

27. DAVIS, N. T. 1956. The morphology and functional anatomy of the male and female reproductive systems of *Cimex lectularius* L. (Heteroptera: Cimicidae). *Ann. Ent. Soc. Amer.* **49**: 466–93.

28. DETHIER, V. G. 1953. Chemoreception. In *Insect Physiology*. K. D. Roeder ed., Wiley, New York, pp. 544–76.

29. DEWITZ, J. 1886. Über der Setzmussigkeit in der Ortsveränderung der Spermatozoon und in der Vereinigung derselben mit dem Ei. *Archiv. ges. Physiol.* **38**: 358–85.

G   R. I.

30. DOUTT, R. L.   1959.   The biology of parasitic Hymenoptera. *Ann. Rev. Ent.* **4**: 161–82.

31. DOWNES, J. A.   1958.   Assembly and mating in the biting Nematocera.   *Proc. 10th Int. Cong. Ent.* **2**: 425–34.

32. EDWARDS, J. S.   1961.   On the reproduction of *Prionoplus reticularis* (Coleoptera, Cerambycidae), with general remarks on reproduction in the Cerambycidae.   *Quart. J. Micr. Sci.* **102**: 519–30.

33. ENGELMANN, F.   1960.   Mechanisms controlling reproduction in two viviparous cockroaches (Blattaria).   *Ann. N.Y. Acad. Sci.* **89**: 516–36.

34. ——— 1962.   Further experiments on the regulation of the sexual cycle in females of *Leucophaea maderae* (Blattaria).   *Gen. Comp. Endocrinol.* **2**: 183–92.

35. FLANDERS, S. E.   1939.   Environmental control of sex in hymenopterous insects.   *Ann. Ent. Soc. Amer.* **32**: 11–16.

36. ——— 1945.   The role of the spermatophore in the mass propagation of *Macrocentrus ancylivorus*.   *J. Econ. Ent.* **38**: 323.

37. ——— 1946.   The mechanism of sex control in the honey bee.   *J. Econ. Ent.* **39**: 379–80.

38. GILLETT, J. D.   1956.   Initiation and promotion of ovarian development in the mosquito *Aedes* (*Stegomyia*) *aegypti* (Linnaeus).   *Ann. Trop. Med. & Parasitol.* **50**: 375–80.

39. GRESSON, R. A. R. and THREADGOLD, L. T.   1960.   An electron microscope study of bacteria in the oocytes and follicle cells of *Blatta orientalis*.   *Quart. J. Micr. Sci.* **101**: 295–7.

40. HAGAN, H. R.   1931.   The embryogeny of the polyctenid *Hesperoctenes fumarius* Westwood, with reference to viviparity in insects.   *J. Morph.* **51**: 1–117.

41. ——— 1951. *The Embryology of the viviparous insects*.   Ronald Press, New York.   492 pp.

42. HAMILTON, A. G.   1955.   Parthenogenesis in the desert locust (*Schistocerca gregaria* Forsk.) and its possible effect on the maintenance of the species.   *Proc. Roy. Ent. Soc. London A* **30**: 103–14.

43. HARTLEY, J. C.   1961.   The shell of acridid eggs.   *Quart. J. Micr. Sci.* **102**: 249–56.

44. HEBERDEY, R. F.   1931.   Zur Entwicklungsgeschichte vergleichenden Anatomie und Physiologie der weiblichen Geschlechtsausfurwege der Insekten.   *Zeits. Morph. Okol. Tiere.* **22**: 416–586.

45. HEWER, H. R.   1934.   Studies in *Zygaena* (Lepidoptera).   Part II. The mechanism of copulation and the passage of the sperm in the female.   *Proc. Zool. Soc. London* **104**: 513–27.

46. HIGHNAM, K. C. 1961. The histology of the neurosecretory system of the adult female desert locust, *Schistocerca gregaria*. *Quart. J. Micr. Sci.* **102**: 27–38.

47.   1962. Variations in neurosecretory activity during oocyte development in *Schistocerca gregaria*. *J. Endocrinol.* **24**, IV-V.

48.   1962. Neurosecretory control of ovarian development in the desert locust. *Quart. J. Micr. Sci.* **103**: 57–72.

49. HIGHNAM, K. C. and LUSIS, O. 1962. The influence of mature males on the neurosecretory control of ovarian development in the desert locust. *Quart. J. Micr. Sci.* **103**: 73–84.

50. HILL, L. 1962. Neurosecretory control of haemolymph protein concentration during ovarian development in the desert locust. *J. Ins. Physiol.* **8**: 609–19.

51. HINTON, H. E. 1960. Plastron respiration in the eggs of blowflies. *J. Ins. Physiol.* **4**: 176–83.

52.   1960. How some insects, especially the egg stages, avoid drowning when it rains. *Proc. S. Lond. Ent. Nat. Hist. Soc.*, 1960: 138–54.

53.   1962. Respiratory systems of insect egg-shells. *Science Progress* **50**: 96–112.

54.   1963. Sperm transfer in insects and the evolution of haemocoelic insemination. In *Insect Reproduction. Symp. Roy. Ent. Soc. London.* In the press.

55. IMMS, A. D. 1957. *A General Text-book of Entomology*, 9th ed. (Revised by O. W. Richards and R. G. Davies). Methuen & Co., Ltd., London. 886 pp.

56. JACOBS, W. 1953. Verhaltensbiologische Studien an Feldheuschrecken. *Zeits. Tierpsychol.*, Suppl. **1**: 1–228.

57. JOHANSSON, A. S. 1955. The relationship between corpora allata and reproductive organs in starved female *Leucophaea maderae* (Blattaria). *Biol. Bull.* **108**: 40–4.

58. KARLSON, P. Chemistry and biochemistry of insect hormones. *Angew. Chem.* (Int. Ed.) **2**: 175–82.

59. KARLSON, P. and BUTENANDT, A. 1959. Pheromones (Ectohormones) in insects. *Ann. Rev. Ent.* **4**: 39–58.

60. KAYE, J. S. 1962. Acrosome formation in the house cricket. *J. Cell. Biol.* **12**: 411–31.

61. KERR, W. E. 1962. The genetics of sex determination. *Ann. Rev. Ent.* **7**: 157–76.

62. KHALIFA, A. 1949. The mechanism of insemination and the mode of action of the spermatophore in *Gryllus domesticus*. *Quart. J. Micr. Sci.* **90**: 281–92.

63.   1950. Spermatophore production in *Galleria melonella* L. (Lepidoptera). *Proc. Roy. Ent. Soc. London A* **25**: 33.

64. KHALIFA, A.   1950.   Spermatophore production and egg-laying behaviour in *Rhodnius prolixus*.   *Parasitology* **40**: 283–9.

65. KING, R. C. and DEVINE, R. L.   1958.   Oogenesis in adult *Drosophila melanogaster*.   VII.   The submicroscopic morphology of the ovary.   *Growth* **22**: 299–326.

66. KING, R. C., ROBINSON, A. C. and SMITH, R. F.   1956.   Oogenesis in adult *Drosophila melanogaster*.   *Growth* **20**:   121–57.

67. KNIPLING, E. F.   1960.   The eradication of the screw-worm fly.   *Scientific American* **203**:   54–61.

68. LANDA, V.   1961.   Use of an artificial spermatophore in the study of the activation of the spermatozoa and development of the spermatophore in the cockchafer.   *Nature* **190**: 935–6.

69. LEES, A. D.   1960.   The role of photoperiod and temperature in the determination of the parthenogenetic and sexual forms in the aphid *Megoura viciae* Buckton.   II.   The operation of the 'interval timer' in young clones.   *J. Ins. Physiol.* **4**:   154–75.

70. ——— 1961. Clonal polymorphism in aphids.   *Symp. Roy. Ent. Soc. London* **1**:   68–79.

71. LeFEUVRE, W. P.   1939.   A phasmid with spermatophore.   *Proc. Roy. Ent. Soc. London A* **14**: 24.

72. LEIBY, R. W.   1929.   Polyembryony in insects.   *Trans. IVth Internat. Congr. Ent.* Ithaca 1928 **2**: 873–87.

73. LOHER, W.   1960.   The chemical acceleration of the maturation process and its hormonal control in the male of the desert locust.   *Proc. Roy. Soc. London B* **153**:   380–97.

74. LÜSCHER, M.   1961.   Social control of polymorphism in termites.   *Symp. Roy. Ent. Soc. London* **1**:   43–56.

75. LUSIS, O.   1963.   The histology and histochemistry of development and resorption in the terminal oocytes of the desert locust. *Schistocerca gregaria*.   *Quart. J. Micr. Sci.* **104**:   57–68.

76. MANTON, S. M.   1938.   The passage of spermatozoa into the ovary in *Peripatopsis*.   *Phil. Trans. Roy. Soc.* (B) **228**:   421–44.

77. McFARLANE, J. E.   1962.   The cuticles of the egg of the house cricket.   *Can. J. Zool.* **40**:   13–21.

78. McFARLANE, J. E., GHOURI, A. S. K. and KENNARD, C. P. 1959. Water absorption by the eggs of crickets.   *Can. J. Zool.* **37**: 391–9.

79. NATH, V., GUPTA, B. L. and BAINS, G. S.   1958.   Histochemical and morphological studies of the lipids in oogenesis.   V.   The egg-follicle of *Culex fatigans*.   *Res. Bull. Panjab. Univ.* **148**: 135–48a.

80. NATH, V., GUPTA, B. L. and LAL, B.   1958.   Histochemical and morphological studies of the lipids in oogenesis.   I. *Periplaneta americana*.   *Quart. J. Micr. Sci.* **99**:   315–32.

81. NATH, V., GUPTA, B. L. and MITTAL, L. C.   1960.   Position of the proximal centriole in flagellate spermatozoa. *Nature* **186**: 899–900.

82. NATH, V., GUPTA, B. L. and SEHGAL, P.   1957.   Mitochondria and Golgi bodies in the spermatogenesis of *Periplaneta americana* as studied under the phase-contrast microscope.   *Res. Bull. Panjab. Univ.* **112**: 317–26.

83. NAYAR, K. K.   1958.   Studies in the neurosecretory system of *Iphita limbata* Stahl. V.   Probable endocrine basis of oviposition in the female insect.   *Proc. Ind. Acad. Sci.* B **47**: 233–51.

84. NAYAR, J. K.   1963.   Effect of synthetic ' queen substance ' (9-oxodec-trans-2-enoic acid) on ovary development in the housefly, *Musca domestica* L.   *Nature* **197**: 923–4.

85. NEILSON, E. T.   1959.   Copulation of *Glyptotendipes* (*Phytotendipes*) *paripes*.   *Nature* **184**: 1252–3.

86. NONIDEZ, J. F.   1920.   Internal phenomena of reproduction i n *Drosophila*.   *Biol. Bull.* **39**: 210–30.

87. NORRIS, M. J.   1932.   Contributions towards the study of insect fertility. I.   The structure and operation of the reproductive organs of the genera *Ephestia* and *Plodia*.   *Proc. Zool. Soc. London* **102**: 595–611.

88. NUR, U.   1962.   Sperms, sperm bundles and fertilization in a mealy bug, *Pseudococcus obscurus* Essig (Homoptera: Coccoidea).   *J. Morph.* **111**: 173–84.

89. OMURA, S.   1936.   Studies on the reproductive system of *Bombyx mori*. I.   Structure of the testis and the intra-testicular behaviour of the spermatozoa.   *J. Fac. Agric. Hokkaido Imp. Univ.* **38**: 151–81.

90. ——   1938.   Structure and function of the female genital system of *Bombyx mori*, with special reference to the mechanism of fertilization.   *J. Fac. Agric. Hokkaido Imp. Univ.* **40**: 111–28.

91. ——   1938.   Post-testicular organs and post-testicular behaviour of the spermatozoa in *Bombyx mori*.   *J. Fac. Agric. Hokkaido Imp. Univ.* **40**: 129–70.

92. PAYNE, M. A.   1933.   The structure of the testis and movement of sperms in *Chortophaga viridifasciata* as demonstrated by intravitam technique.   *J. Morph.* **54**: 321–46.

93. ——   1934.   Intravitam studies on the Hemipteran, *Leptocoris trivittatus*.   A description of the male reproductive system and turning of the sperms.   *J. Morph.* **56**: 513–32.

94. PERDECK, A. C.   1957.   The isolating value of specific song patterns in two sibling species of grasshoppers.   *Behaviour* **12**: 1–75.

95. PRYOR, M. G. M. 1940. On the hardening of the ootheca of *Blatta orientalis*. *Proc. Roy. Soc. London B* **128**: 393–407.

96. PRYOR, M. G. M., RUSSELL, P. B. and TODD, A. R. 1946. Protocatechuic acid, the substance responsible for the hardening of the cockroach ootheca. *Biochem. J.* **40**: 627–8.

97. QUO, F. 1959. Studies in the reproduction of the oriental migratory locust. The physiological effects of castration and copulation. *Acta Ent. Sinica* **9**: 464–76 (Chinese: English summary).

98. RAABE, M. 1959. Neurohormones chez les insectes. *Bull. Soc. Zool. Fr.* **84**: 272–316.

99. ROEDER, K. D. 1935. An experimental analysis of the sexual behaviour of the praying mantis (*Mantis religiosa* L.). *Biol. Bull.* **69**: 203–20.

100. ROTH, L. M. 1948. A study of mosquito behaviour. An experimental laboratory study of the sexual behaviour of *Aedes aegypti* (Linnaeus). *Am. Midland Nat.* **40**: 265–352.

101. ROTH, L. M. and WILLIS, E. R. 1954. The reproduction of cockroaches. *Smithsonian Misc. Coll.* **122**: 1–49.

102. ROTHENBUHLER, W. C., GOWER, J. W. and PARK, O. W. 1952. Androgenesis with zygogenesis in gynandromorphic honey bees (*Apis mellifera* L.).

103. ROTHSCHILD, LORD. 1955. The spermatozoa of the honey bee. *Trans. Roy. Ent. Soc. London* **107**: 289.

104. SCHLOTTMAN, L. L. and BONHAG, P. F. 1956. Histology of the ovary of the adult mealworm *Tenebrio molitor* L. *Univ. California Publ. Ent.* **11**: 351–94.

105. SCHMIDT, E. L. and WILLIAMS, C. M. 1953. Physiology of insect diapause. V. Assay of the growth and differentiation hormone of Lepidoptera by the method of tissue culture. *Biol. Bull.* **105**: 174–87.

106. SCHNEIRLA, T. C. 1953. Basic problems in the nature of insect behaviour. In *Insect Physiology*. K. D. Roeder, ed. Wiley, New York, pp. 656–85.

107. SLIFER, E. H. 1954. Changes in certain of the grasshopper egg coverings during development as indicated by fast green and other dyes. *J. Exp. Zool.* **110**: 183–204.

108. SMITH, S. G. 1960. Cytogenetics of insects. *Ann. Rev. Ent.* **5**: 69–84.

109. SNODGRASS, R. E. 1935. *The Principles of Insect Morphology*. McGraw-Hill Book Co., Ltd., New York.

110. ——— 1957. A revised interpretation of the external reproductive organs of male insects. *Smithsonian Misc. Coll.* **135**, no. 5, 107 pp.

111. STRANGWAYS-DIXON, J. 1961. The relationship between nutrition, hormones and reproduction in the blowfly *Calliphora erythrocephala* (Meig.). II. The effect of removing the ovaries, the corpus allatum and the median neurosecretory cells upon selective feeding and the demonstration of the corpus allatum cycle. *J. Exp. Biol.* **38**: 637–46.

112. —— 1962. The relationship between nutrition, hormones and reproduction in the blowfly *Calliphora erythrocephala* (Meig.). III. The corpus allatum in relation to nutrition, the ovaries, innervation and the corpus cardiacum. *J. Exp. Biol.* **39**: 293–306.

113. SUOMALAINEN, E. 1962. Significance of parthenogenesis in the evolution of insects. *Ann. Rev. Ent.* **7**: 349–66.

114. TABER, S. and BLUM, M. S. 1960. Preservation of honey bee semen. *Science* **131**: 1734–5.

115. TELFER, W. H. 1954. Immunological studies of insect metamorphosis. II. The role of a sex-limited blood protein in egg formation by the *Cecropia* silkworm. *J. Gen. Physiol.* **37**: 539–58.

116. —— 1960. The selective accumulation of blood proteins by the oocytes of Saturniid moths. *Biol. Bull.* **118**: 338–51.

117. —— 1961. The route of entry and localization of blood proteins in the oocytes of Saturniid moths. *J. Biophys. Biochem. Cytol.* **9**: 747–59.

118. TELFER, W. H. and RUTBERG, L. D. 1960. The effects of blood protein depletion on the growth of the oocytes in the *Cecropia* moth. *Biol. Bull.* **118**: 352–66.

119. TELFER, W. H. and WILLIAMS, C. M. 1952. The relation of the blood proteins to egg formation in the *Cecropia* silkworm. *Anat. Rec.* **113**: 82.

120. THOMSEN, E. 1952. Functional significance of neurosecretory cells of adult *Calliphora*. *J. Exp. Biol.* **29**: 137–72.

121. THOMSEN, E. and MØLLER, I. 1959. Further studies on the function of the neurosecretory brain cells of the adult *Calliphora* female. *The Ontogeny of insects*, pp. 121–6. I. Hrdý, ed. *Czech. Acad. Sci.*, Prague.

122. TUFT, P. H. 1950. The structure of the insect egg-shell in relation to the respiration of the embryo. *J. Exp. Biol.* **26**: 327–34.

123. VIRKKI, N. 1956. Zur Kenntnis der postmeiotischen Ereignisse der Sämenentwicklung bei dem Skarabäiden (Coleoptera). *Zeits. Zellforsch.* **44**: 644–65.

124. WEIDNER, H. 1934. Beitrage zur Morphologie und Physiologie des Genitalapparates der weiblichen Lepidopteren. *Z. angew. Ent.* **21**: 239–90.

125. WHITE, M. J. D.   1946.   The chromosome cycle and spermato-
    genesis of *Miastor*. *J. Morph.* **79**: 323–69.

126. WHITING, P. W.   1945.   Evolution of male haploidy.   *Quart.
    Rev. Biol.* **20**: 231–60.

127. WIGGLESWORTH, V. B.   1936.   The function of the corpus allatum
    in the growth and reproduction of *Rhodnius prolixus*. *Quart. J.
    Micr. Sci.* **79**: 91–120.

128.   1954.   *The Physiology of Insect Metamorphosis*.   Cambridge
    University Press, 152 pp.

129.   1955.   *The Principles of Insect Physiology*, 5th ed.   Methuen and
    Co., London.

130.   1963.   The juvenile hormone effect of farnesol and some related
    compounds: quantitative experiments. *J. Ins. Physiol.* **9**:
    105–19.

131. WIGGLESWORTH, V. B. and BEAMENT, J. W. L.   1950.   The res-
    piratory mechanism of some insect eggs.   *Quart. J. Micr.
    Sci.* **91**: 429–52.

132. WIGGLESWORTH, V. B. and SALPETER, M. M.   1962.   The aero-
    scopic chorion of the egg of *Calliphora erythrocephala* studied
    with the electron microscope. *J. Ins. Physiol.* **8**: 635–42.

133. WILLIAMS, C. M.   1956.   The juvenile hormone of insects.   *Nature*
    178: 212–13.

134.   1961.   The juvenile hormone.   II.   Its role in the endocrine
    control of molting, pupation and adult development in the
    Cecropia silkworm.   *Biol. Bull.* **121**: 572–84.

135. WRIGHT, R. H.   1963.   Molecular vibration and insect sex attrac-
    tants.   *Nature* **198**: 455–9.

136. YASUZUMI, G. and ISHIDA, H.   1957.   Spermatogenesis in animals
    as revealed by electron microscopy.   II.   Submicroscopic
    structure of developing spermatid nuclei of grasshoppers. *J.
    Biophys. Biochem. Cytol.* **3**: 663–8.

Index